Mathematics Lessons for the Sixth Grade

by

Ernst Schuberth

AWSNA

Published by:
The Association of Waldorf Schools of North America
3911 Bannister Road
Fair Oaks, CA 95628

Title: Mathematics Lessons for the Sixth Grade
Author: Ernst Schuberth
© 2002 by AWSNA
ISBN # 1-888365-37-4
German Title: *Der Mathematikunterricht in der sechsten Klasse an Waldorfschulen*
Original ISBN: 3-7725-0266-0
Printed by: Verlag Freies Geistesleben
English edition published with permission of the author
Translators: Thomas Forman and others
Editor: David Mitchell
Proofreader: Ann Erwin
Cover: Hallie Wootan

Curriculum Series

The Publications Committee of AWSNA is pleased to bring forward this publication as part of its Curriculum Series. The thoughts and ideas represented herein are solely those of the author and do not necessarily represent any implied criteria set by AWSNA. It is our intention to stimulate as much writing and thinking as possible about our curriculum, including diverse views. Please contact us with feedback on this publication as well as requests for future work.

David S. Mitchell
For the Publications Committee
AWSNA

Table of Contents

Preface

The following pages are intended as a contribution to implementing curriculum indications on mathematics given by Rudolf Steiner. They are offered to enlarge on my short essay on elementary instruction in mathematics in Waldorf schools.[1] Just as in the latter work, specific suggestions are to be taken in each case as just that; they are not intended to contradict other ideas. It is of particular importance that the various elements that contribute to teaching are understood based on a solid understanding of the developmental stages of childhood and pedagogy. A short chapter about the developmental situation of sixth graders and another on the overall curriculum of this grade precede the technical discussions of the sixth grade curriculum. Here I make some assumptions and omit explanations of the structure of a Waldorf schools and the elementary concepts of human development. The reader can easily find this background in the ample literature dealing with Waldorf schools.[2]

The principal subjects are closely connected through the person of the class teacher. He or she can understand how the subjects are related in their pedagogical function. Much of importance may be missing, or even be misunderstood, in our discussions, because these connections can be only briefly indicated here. The trained teacher will, however, recognize my intent. Understanding the developmental stage of the twelve-year-old child affords the possibility to exchange content between subjects or to seek different placements of emphasis—as long as the knowledge of human nature is taken into account.

An important concern of this book is to use Rudolf Steiner's indications regarding early economics instruction. In particular this is brought through interest calculations. Much of our discussions deals with this. The receptivity of children of this age for questions regarding their social surroundings has been demonstrated repeatedly in the course of my own teaching experience. Elementary observations can give the child a first understanding of much that plays a determining role in life. This will connect the child more closely, and with more understanding, to the world.

The role of mathematics instruction must, as already stated, be considered in connection with all other subjects. Economics and sociology are woven into the Waldorf curriculum for this age group, albeit not yet as specially named subjects. A teacher should recognize the connections between different subjects. After all, sociology is a subject where all that has been learned keeps coming together!

Many resources found in existing literature are identified in their place in the text. Here we only wish to thankfully acknowledge the writings of Arnold Bernhard, Ernst Blindel and Louis Locher-Ernst.[3]

I have to thank Dr. Benediktus Hadrop for his critical review of the manuscript and for his innumerable suggestions based on years of mutual contact. In many respects it is due to him that economics, and in particular accounting, has received increased attention within the Waldorf school movement. This approach leads genetically to an understanding of dual entry bookkeeping, among other things. I must also thank Mr. Uwe Schröder of Bielefeld for numerous pointers and critical questions. He read the text with great care. Here I also owe especial thanks to Mrs. Roswitha Bauer. She never tired of patiently re-examining the text, adding improvements, and she came to terms with many a malicious trick played by the modern computer. I am thankful to my friend and colleague Georg Glöckler, the leader of the mathematical-astronomical section at the Goetheanum in Dornach, Switzerland. This book owes a debt of thanks to his ongoing work, carried as it is by deep spiritual impulses. The author also appreciates all reports, pointers, and suggestions for changes given by colleagues, based on their practical work. Interesting new task formulations and beautiful problem sequences are most welcome on a continuous basis.

I would like to add my special gratitude to David Mitchell, Chairman of AWSNA Publications, for his friendship, his editorial help, and his overall support. My thanks also to Tom Forman for his translation.

It has been wonderful for me to experience the United States annually since 1990 when Astrid Schmitt-Stegmann invited me to teach at the Rudolf Steiner College. Most summers I have spent at least four weeks working with American elementary and high school teachers at different places throughout North America. In contrast to my experience in many other countries I find a very deep understanding of economical and social questions. The open minds of my colleagues led to many discussions from which I have learned a lot. Many thanks to all these colleagues.

— Ernst Schuberth
Autumn 2002

The Sixth Grade

A flower with unopened flower petals points to the two directions of its development—to the preceding seed and bud and to the future flower and fruit. In the same way, in his particular stage of development, the child must be understood as pointing back to its preceding stage of development as well as to the dormant future. What preceded the child's present situation in the sixth grade and what, at this point in time, is heralded?

By the twelfth year the child has already gone through important stages of development. During the preschool period he has, by imitation, gained the basic human abilities of walking, talking, and early thinking. Guided by his teachers he has acquired the elementary techniques of culture and—given appropriate guidance—an aesthetic/artistic sense for colors, sounds, and forms in the world. With open soul he has entered fields that his educators have presented as worthwhile. An inner process of assimilation has taken place resulting in a condensation of the educators' offerings into his own soul-being. Based on the plant's inherent formative forces, it grows into light and air. Similarly the schoolchild lives in an opening gesture in which learning also signifies nourishment and self-formation.

Yet, at this time and from the direction of the future, the age of the youth already knocks at the door. Just as the green of sepals in the plant recedes, making way for a manifold and colorful shine, so too does a much more individual dawning of soul-life start to take place in the youth. This surrounds his inner space like the sheath of the flower that blossoms. The simple and steady devotion to the sun's light is followed by a flashing up of colorful splendor, of streaming fragrance, and of future fruit formation. These are now the focis of the plant's development. In the youth one can well compare the dawn of soul activity, combined with a very individual and protected inwardness, with the blossoming of the plant.

Should one wish to correlate the image of the development of the plant with that of the child in its twelfth year—however inadequate the comparison—one can think of the formation of the bud. From the outside it still looks green like a leaf; however it can only be understood in its formative process by keeping in mind the flowering that is yet to come.[4] In this way a seed starts to sprout functionally in the soul-life of the child. This process can, by its very nature, be understood only when viewed from the age of youth. Without characterizing the whole gamut of phenomena by its essential being, the commonly used expression *pre*-puberty points to such a relationship. As for the soul, the age of youth is characterized by a growing independence of the inner life. No longer are truth, beauty, and goodness accepted as judged by another person; the young human being now wishes to exercise his or her own judgment when it comes to the assignment of such high ideals. The rejecting gesture—the hedge of thorns around the sleeping beauty in Grimm's fairy tale—protects the tender soul content of the young person. This gesture can surface at special moments—mostly in relation to peers. Now the educator can only give indications toward seeing this world while gaining experience. He is able to show how one can sort phenomena by thinking and how practiced skill can yield satisfactory results in real life. The age of youth asks the educator for knowledge of the world and a connection with the present time.

One inner ability in particular heralds the arrival of early youth. It is the ability to think logically. It has often been described how *prior* to this age the child fails to notice logical inconsistencies. For instance Martin Wagenschein describes how children answer the question, "Whence comes the wind?" with "from the moving trees." The next question, "Where does the movement of the trees come from?" they reply to with no hesitation by pointing to the wind.[5] Prior to this developmental change, some children even invent rather complicated machines, based on such circular thinking, thus approaching the perpetuum mobile. At this age one of my children asked me to install an electric motor in my car. I should start the car with the petrol engine which in turn would get the current from the dynamo. The latter after all, delivers current when one is traveling full speed. If the child has passed the described change in development, he is unable to give a reason why this is incorrect but he will have a strong feel for the inconsistency and reject it. The psychologist Jean Piaget talked about a period of formal procedures reached by children of this age.[6] A rubicon has been crossed in development, the new is already recognizable. The world wants to be seen as a logically constructed world.

This inward tendency, the experience of thoughts and their correlations in one's own inner being, combines with a stronger need to understand the natural and cultural conditions of life more consciously. The class teacher in the Waldorf school is still the guardian and guiding personality who now has to provide guidance to their own judgments. At this time the rumbling in the souls of the children is the distant lightning of the upheavals that reach their culmination with the actual age of youth.

These events can be described more realistically and truthfully using anthroposophical concepts of anthropology. This allows a deeper understanding of the developmental situation of the child. Here is how Rudolf Steiner characterizes it:

> Between the ages of twelve and thirteen, there occurs an important point in the development of the child. At that time the human being's soul-spiritual being gains strength and power insofar as this soul-spiritual part is less dependent on the ego. What we have become accustomed to call the astral body in spiritual science strengthens and combines with the etheric body. In fact the astral body's real birth as an independent unity occurs only fully with sexual maturity, yet it makes its presence felt through the etheric body in a peculiar manner by strengthening and pervading it between the twelfth and thirteenth years of life. This is another important stage in the course of development. If we know how to treat the innate ability correctly, this finds expression in the beginnings of development of understanding for the external impulses that work in the world. These are similar to the soul-spiritual impulses. This is manifested, for example, in the way that these impulses work as forces in history.[7]

Thus the closer relationship of the astral body to the etheric body leads to unique soul configurations during pre-puberty.

The soul forces used to grasp historical impulses are related to the forces we use to grasp workings of the physical laws within the human organism. The historical impulses determine us as cultural beings, the physical ones as beings belonging to nature. "There exists a kinship between understanding concepts of historical impulses within mankind and concepts of external physical impulses of nature in the human organism. The essence of being truly human lives in the historical impulses. Yet what is gathered within these impulses acts as the outer progression of history and in turn acts on the human being. If you describe the human eye, the same forces that work in nature also work within the human being. The same sort of understanding needs to be applied to both processes, and this understanding really starts only in the twelfth year of life."[8] Questions about social life, like the ones to be discussed later in this book, can be approached in the same manner.

An overview of the entire development of the student shows that the last third of the time with the class teacher (in the sense of Waldorf education) forms, in some respects, a polar opposite to the first third. The first was under the sign of a loving involvement with the authority of the teacher. On the way to independence many distancing shocks are needed. The class teacher can bring the same love and understanding to these which he managed to bring to the love of the children as an objective factor in their development during the first years of school.

Furthering the connection to the world is part of the educational task regarding the child's astral body—next to addressing its powers of judgment. At this time the class teacher should meet the children as a person who is open to the world and has many interests. What part of the historical evolution of the world and of today's situation has been a determining factor for my life? What limitations are placed on my potential spheres of action by natural law? Can I use my understanding of these laws to understand my surroundings and perhaps invent something new? The dawn of the children's awakening intellect can fill the teacher with enthusiasm to look anew at the surrounding world he has known for so long and to discover something new in it every day. The class teacher's "higher grades" start with the sixth grade and make him the children's contemporary with regard to curriculum content. It goes without saying that the class teacher cannot be an expert on all questions. Interests and the ability to ask the right questions are more important than detailed knowledge. The non-mathematician, physicist, chemist, or historian is the very one with the possibility to walk into the world with the child and stimulate questions. The expert often cannot really do this.

I would like to share two personal experiences. The first one is the deep gratitude toward my own class teacher, Elizabeth Banzer, from Hanover, Germany. Especially in the field of natural science she had little training, yet she faced everything new with never-tiring interest and through this very fact evoked interest for the world in her students. This interest has had a more enduring effect than all the particulars that were studied. The second experience involves my own activity as a class teacher after my university training in mathematics and physics. To start with, the children in my class were far more interested in history, grammar, and other subjects that I did not study than in the ones I studied. There everything was clear and logical. Many teachers in the high school, who were also class teachers, have shared this same observation with me.

These experiences can explain the great difference between the "middle school grades" of the class teacher and the high school (grades 9 to 12). The high school student demands mastery of the subject and clear exposition from the educator. The teacher should be a competent partner. During the last year with the class teacher the child wants to develop his or her own powers of judgment under the guidance of the teacher. The student at this age wants to be allowed to test his abilities—even when in error, and he wants to be guided toward independence. It goes without saying that this wish is not consciously expressed.

Some Items from the Sixth Grade Curriculum

A Waldorf teacher responds to the described stage of development in varied ways, and each subject contributes to the inner development of the child in its own characteristic way. The soul organism of the child is an interconnected organism, and the curriculum should also be seen as an organism. The different subjects relate to each other like organs and are aimed at a whole organism, namely the child, at its specific stage of development. The following remarks are aimed at these commonalities.

History

History, in the sixth grade, describes the times of the ascendancy of the Greek and Roman cultures and also shows their decline. It leads to the Middle Ages and the Crusades, the development of the culture of cities, the monastic ways of the Occident, and the the seeds of modern times as they become visible under the reign of the Hohenstaufen dynasty. Changes begin to form at the time of the Crusades. These changes are imposed on the Occident by the encounter with a non-Christian culture and by a conscious coming to terms with foreign ideas. The knightly order, and particularly the Templars, is responsible for an impulse toward the structuring of society and more global economic cooperation. The growth of influence of the Hansa and the German order in the space of the Baltic Sea and the North Sea gives rise to a political system in the north which—however questionable any form of totalitarianism may be—

develops more spatially-extended, political, economic, and cultural ways of thinking. What later centuries perfect as securely mastered arts is now developed gropingly. By the degree that individual logical judgment gains in breadth and might, the traditional authority loses power. During the sixth year of school the child is made to see how mankind in its cultural development has progressed along the same road that he now must travel as an individual. The student's progress in individual developmental makes him or her a conscious participant in a surrounding world, formed by history which puts a stamp on both the individual and his generation.

Physics

Beside history which demonstrates connections, natural science demands to be treated systematically. During the year prior to high school the principal subjects of physics are presented, starting with acoustics, optics, theory of heat, theory of electricity and magnetism, and then mechnics in the seventh grade. Now the child learns for the first time how conformity to laws governing changing phenomena may be methodically discovered. For example, a constant factor may be found in the manifold possibilities of sounding a quarter note on an instrument, namely the ratio of lengths 4 : 3. Yet this law allows an infinite variation of interpretations that create the uniqueness of each voice.

The experiences of the first acoustic lessons may be methodically applied in all the areas of physics: to find common laws, and, as well, to discover the gamut of individual interpretations in art, technical areas, and nature. In this way the children, with their growing abilities, learn to judge and to recognize commonalities in the individual cases of laws, without falling prey to the error that knowing one law encompasses the reach of all phenomena.

Grammar

The focus of grammar is sentence structure. The mutual relationship of the parts of a sentence reveals a logical element more universal than the thought of the predicate. The conjunctions in particular (if, because, and so forth) express basic categories of thought. They connect the statements of the various sentences with each other in different ways.

By understanding these different relationships, the child gets away from expressed content and grasps thought structures which themselves lack imaginable content. This forms a foundation for unbiased thinking without which an entire layer of language and thoughts would be obscured.

Then again the recourse to general laws of language is countered when attention is turned to the wealth of embodiments of language and one first becomes aware of the stylistic differences between different poets. The individual stamps imposed by the way poets choose to express themselves, as well as their artistic nuances, increasingly occupy center stage in the next years of school.

The impulse to begin to develop conceptual thinking and in pure relationships between concepts may be traced through other subjects in a manner similar to the above examples. The same basic steps are required in every case: the search for the universal in the specific and the emergence of the specific details out of the universal. In other words, one needs to look for the determining essence in each phenomenon and identify the wealth of embodiments in which a being can reveal itself. One could call these two moves *generalizing* and *concretizing*. If recognizing the law is directed toward deeper understanding of a known, concretizing and individualizing require *imagination*. The power of imagination lets us form new creations. The contrast between imagination and will, between memory and imagination, is dealt with in detail in the first lectures of *The Study of Man*.[9]

In the organism of its subjects, mathematics, too, picks up this theme. One can look at algebra as a school of unbiased thinking, in the same way presented by grammar but from a slightly different point of view. Algebra accomplishes this with its description of relationships between calculating procedures that is independent of concrete numerical concepts. Geometry contains in veritably ideal form the named basic gestures of thinking. Here we find wonderful possibilities between universal statements—for example, the Pythagorean theorem—and the beauty of movement of specific forms. This will be discussed in more detail elsewhere.[10] But let as take a look at the content of the mathematics curriculum in the preceding years.

The Three Stages of the Mathematics Curriculum in Grades 1 to 8

In the second seven-year period the child goes through three different stages of development. In each one a different relationship of the soul-spiritual to the corporeal-bodily is being formed.[11] The transitions take place roughly in the third grade, when the child is ten years old, and in the fifth or sixth grade, when the child is in the twelfth year. In both cases Rudolf Steiner speaks of a rubicon, the crossing of which leads to fundamental changes compared to the preceding phase of life. The first transition brings about a strengthening of ego consciousness which finds expression with the child facing his surroundings in a more conscious manner. This may involve crises regarding authority in relationhips with the teachers. Also all sorts of moral uncertainties, even petty thefts and consciously constructed lies, may occur. The child emerges from these crises with a more conscious way of seeing the world.

As already mentioned, the second transition brings the astral body into closer relationship with the etheric body.[12] An awakening of logical thinking may now be observed. The child inwardly experiences correlations in her own thoughts that are also at work in the outer world. What is grasped within the soul, the thoughts, gives her the key to understanding the world and how it hangs together.

The mathematics curriculum meets these stages of development like the other subjects by placing the focus of attention in each section in a way that may be roughly characterized as follows:[13]

Grades 1 to 3

Handling (natural) numbers and elementary calculations provides the principal focus of mathematics in grades 1 to 3. Different operations bring the numbers in characteristically different relationships to each other. Their inner gestures allow the operations to relate to specific temperaments such that they assume a clear inner coloring.[14] Next to a training in numerical conceptualizing special attention will be given to the differentiation between analytical and synthetical processes. This is accomplished by subdividing on one hand and by grouping numbers over the different operations on the other. Along with this much emphasis is placed on training memory by acquiring knowlege of elementary addition and the minor multiplication tables. In third grade the acquired skills are applied to word problems, i.e. calculating with given quantities.

In this section we see numbers as individual concepts and the relationships they enter by means of different operations as the principal focus. Little attention is paid to general laws.

Grades 4 and 5

During the second stage—approximately grades 4 and 5—emphasis is placed on calculating with fractions. Fractions result when numbers (natural or whole) relate to each other. To use them for arithmetical operations involves calculating with numbers which themselves have resulted from other calculations. Although rules for such arithmetic calculations are developed and defined, the actual individual fractions or relationships take center stage. According to the Waldorf curriculum the child understands animals and plants based on their relationships to each other and to the human being. In mathematics, too, relationships are the center of observation. When teaching geometry a comparison of different forms is studied. For example, the square, a perfect quadrangle, is used to characterize the different quadrangles based on their relationships to each other and to the square.

Grades 6 to 8

The introduction of algebra provides the most important impact at the beginning of the third stage. We use algebra conventionally by using letters in mathematics (calculation with letters). Of course letters or other symbols may be used earlier as place indictors in calculations. In this third stage, the decisively new function of letters or symbols is the formulation of general laws which describe the dependence of different values to each other or given relationships between mathematical operations.

In this way thinking moves beyond individual concepts and makes a start toward changing its content to purely conceptual connections. This also makes possible thinking in concepts such as "less than nothing," i.e. negative numbers. Additionally, it now becomes possible to think of content that can not be expressed by the relationship of two whole numbers. The student will encounter these in the seventh grade when roots are introduced and also through geometry. Perhaps one could say that algebra establishes a relationship between mathematical operations in the same way that in the first stage numbers came into relation to each other through calculation, or as the numerical relationships related to each other in the second stage.

If we correlated these three stages to everyday life we find the following (from a certain point of view): We most frequently use numbers by themselves when working with similar objects, for instance three apples, four chairs, two forks, and so forth. Here we deal with individual concepts, based on things we perceived with our senses or imagined. We use the numbers to grasp their quantity. The calculations connected with these numbers, too, are, for the most part, accompanied by sensory concepts. Even though this is not quite accurate from other points of view, one can say that the mathematical activities of the first phase, i.e. in grades 1 to 3, are prevalently related to concepts. Nevertheless we base this process on a number of occurrences. Thus our orientation is the will.

When we proceed to the second section (grades 4 and 5), to the fractions and relationships, we no longer deal only with individual numbers but with numerical relationships. All fractions such as $\frac{1}{2}$, $\frac{1}{3}$, $\frac{1}{4}$, but also $\frac{2}{3}$, $\frac{3}{4}$, and so forth, make practical sense only when related to a basic magnitude. $\frac{1}{2}$ by itself cannot define a length unless one adds 1 foot, 1 mile or some other reference. The formation of relationships enters immediately when dealing with fractions which, in its breathing, rhythmic nature, has been nurtured from the first year of school. By bringing two quantities of the same kind in relation to each other (two lengths, two surfaces, two weights), we leave the area of mere objects. The relationship that we express in the proportion is not a tangible object.

Let us demonstrate this with an example. If we have two boards of different lengths, perhaps 3 and 5 feet in length, the *difference* is a board 2 feet long. But the *relation* between them is itself not a piece of board, only a *relation* of the physical magnitude. To determine it we could, in the simplest case, look for a length which could be a measure of both boards when laid end-to-end. If this cannot be done directly, we have to find a third length by which the numerical relationship between the two original lengths can be defined. This sort of measuring and forming of relationships plays a large role in spatial as well as time relationships. The inner mobility of correlations which evokes *feelings* in us lies in the relation between our heartbeat and breathing and in the subdivision of notes in music. Art lives to a large degree in such quantitative, and also qualitative, relationships. One can even say that a sensory impression becomes aesthetic and artistic through the interweaving creation of relationships of sensory qualities and not through the immediate sensory impression. From these points of view one could state that mathematical abilities in the second phase have a particular relation to the life of feelings.

The emphasis in the third phase (grades 6 to 8) is on the introduction of algebra and its applications. This is primarily concerned, as already stated, with the relationships of mathematical operations with each other. These operations are in themselves activities (*operare* = to work). In this connection one has to remember that all of mathematics is connected with the so-called "will-senses."[15] The will-element, active within calculating operations from the very first, is increasingly taken up into the observation of thinking itself. The strengthening of the *will to think* makes this possible. This faculty received its first schooling during the formation of memory in the first stage. Mental arithmetic requires that numerical concepts be purposefully carried out and appropriately connected with each other in accordance to their respective governing laws. As the age of youth approaches these correlations between calculating operations become conscious and thus demand again a stronger force which is more within the soul than it was at the beginning of school-life.

If one observes and compares the three developmental phases in the second seven-year period, one arrives at the above characterization of how the will to think develops. Again, if one compares the second seven-year period with the age of youth, one will have to consider relativities because judgment then has not yet let go of the leadership of authority to the degree that is a matter of course at the age of youth. As is so often the case, here, too, a true picture will depend on the factors that have to be referred to within the particular frame of reference.

The Tasks of Teaching Mathematics in Sixth Grade

Rudolf Steiner does not see the third phase of teaching mathematics described in the previous section as purely a mathematical task. He makes an elemental connection between algebra (letter-calculation) and his elementary teaching of economics. Forms of thought applied in algebra to grasp pure conformance to laws should at first be practiced on relationships that are important when dealing with money. This gives instruction a surprisingly down-to-earth touch which guards against dissolving into pure logical correlations.

In his methodological presentations Rudolf Steiner characterizes the soul condition of children in their twelfth year in connection with the teaching of mathematics in the following way:

> The power of judgment, the ability to rely on the thoughtful, intellectual understanding of people, needs to be addressed at the end of elementary school. This is why in the twelfth year, we work toward a discerning understanding in order to let things come together with that which still requires a degree of instinct. Yet instinct is already strongly overshadowed by the power of judgment. At this time we find, as it were, the dusk conditions of the soul, which need to be overcome by the power of judgment. During this time we need to bear in mind that the human being has an instinct for earning interest, for what can be reaped, for discount, and so forth. All this appeals as instinct. But we must already forcefully drown this with judgment. Therefore, we must place into this time period the relationship that exist between mathematics, the circulation of goods, and the pecuniary circumstances—that is percent calculation, interest calculation, calculating discount, and similar matters.[16]

In his curriculum lectures Steiner briefly summarizes the content of mathematics teaching in sixth grade:

> Then, in the sixth year of school, proceed to interest and percent calculations, to discount calculation, to simple exchange calculation. Use this to create a basis for the letter calculation, as I have shown.[17]

As can be seen, Steiner brings the study of mathematics into close connection with the study of economics because the nature of money, its economic significance and juridical order, need to be understood in a larger framework. The child is being directed to one of the branches of social life, namely the economy. The teacher can deal with this appropriately only in connection with the remaining basic social laws, namely the cultural and the legal ones. This places the demand on the teacher to turn energetically to the periphery of human activity beyond the school environment.[18]

Whether or not some material left over from fifth grade needs to be caught up, the first epoch of mathematics in sixth grade should immediately begin with this grade's central motive. Dealing with interest and exchange calculations demands a meaningful preparation in elementary economics. This could be accompanied by refreshing the skills needed for calculating interest and discounting—such as multiplication and division of fractions and similar material. In the discussions of economics, money— one could say the monetary *process*—should be explained. This includes discussions of how money comes about in connection with the division of labor and the exchange of goods as well as the transformation of human relations within their reciprocal monetary obligations. The part played by money as capital in the creation of means of production also needs to be discussed here. This is significant for the children because it moves them away from thinking of money as the material of the coin or banknote. Increasingly they come to understand how the monetary process between people cannot be grasped simply in terms of things but that one could really say it is a many sided spiritual happening within relationships.

The types of calculations suggested by Steiner only begin to make sense when insights appropriate to a certain age are reached. This is the only way for the child to experience how something about life can be learned by means of mathematics. I have taught sixth grade repeatedly and always notice with astonishment how open children of this age are to such questions, how eagerly they enter the investigation of the development of economic relationships, and how they apply their passionate stand for justice to an embryonic start at bookkeeping.

The path proposed here is based on my work with a sixth grade at the Waldorf school at Mannheim in the school year 1992–93. Charging time worked to account is an activity that seems to me to represent in many ways a natural introduction to an understanding of both thinking along the lines of bookkeeping—in the best sense—as well as understanding money as *global bookkeeping*. Steiner characterized it as such at one time.[19]

Interest calculations then emerge based on discussions of economic questions. This is used to make the transition to letter calculation and beginning algebra. In sixth grade this can be limited to finding simple formulas and their application to practical and mathematical problems.

In sixth grade instruction in proof geometry begins as well. (This will be presented in more detail in a second volume of this work published by AWSNA Publications.) Here dawns the same light as in algebra. Here thinking is used to grasp general valid laws and how they relate to each other. Here we demonstrate how something that is grasped by purely inner activity leads to understanding the outer world. Here, too, logical order is placed side-by-side with imaginative diversity of possible individual phenomena.

In summary, the overall structure of mathematics in the sixth year of school begins with the introduction to elementary economics with particular attention to the monetary system. It transitions to dealing with interest formulae and different applications, and in this ways provides a basis for letter calculations. A few general purely algebraic laws may then conclude the first main lesson block. Calculating with percentages is part of this structure. The second main lesson block may contain a lot of geometry. Then algebra may be taken up again and used to prepare for mathematics in the seventh grade with the formulation of some purely algebraic rules. For example, using the sum of the angles in regular polygons may demonstrate how algebraically definable numerical rules are a possibility in geometry as well.

The Beginning of the Sixth Grade:
The Monetary System/Elementary Economics

The First Week

Only well-planned lessons can do justice to the many subjects of a school term that attempts to develop themes as varied as the monetary system and the economy, as well as arithmetic and algebraic items all together. In order to be true to life we shall approach this part of the curriculum as it builds up over time. In this way different themes appear side by side. Later on we shall treat each theme in greater depth so that their specific contents are kept in context. The range of topics will be presented in a parallel form.

The First Day

Following the shortest possible rhythmic opening, the teacher gives a short preview of this term's theme. This could start by mentioning the many people who make our lives possible. "If we just think of the time we spent today between getting up and the start of school, we find that many people have made it possible that we have soap and towels to wash ourselves, clothes to dress ourselves, food for breakfast, and transportation in order to come to school. We continuously make use of other people's work. People work so that water comes out of the tap, the light goes on, clothes are available, food is purchased at the market, we can drive, and so forth. This main lesson is designed to show how this cooperation of human activities has developed and how it may be justly ordered. With all this some new things will have to be learned in mathematics, because a just order between people also demands conscientious and just compensation. Very often this is done with money, and, for this reason, we shall have a lot to say about money. We measure money with numbers, thus mathematics are of great importance when dealing with money. We shall have to describe laws that govern dealing with money, and this will lead to a new area of mathematics. In this area we shall get to know and and understand *laws* that pervade mathematics. Such laws play an important role in everyday life as well. Along with these laws, thinking is a must for all who wish to be able at some time to design machinery, become an architect, or carry a great responsibility in the economic life. The area of mathematics where one deals with such laws is called *algebra*. The word derives from Arabic and means 'filling up.'[20] In the course of the term we shall address algebra."

In this or a similar manner one can talk to the children about the plans for this main lesson. On this occasion the teacher should feel himself as a citizen of the world possessing a vital and broad interest in all that happens. Of course this interest is not meant in the egoistic sense—not in the sense that one should know how to utilize one's advantages for profit. Rather, it has to address common human interests. After all the weal and woe of entire nations, the difficult north–south and east–west relationships, depend in so many ways on economic and money-related conditions. These relationships are decisive factors.

Following this short introduction a discussion may be started with questions: *What is money and why does one need it? What would our life be like without money?*

This last question can lead to a particularly lively discussion. It can lead to the hypothetical development of an economy in which the self sufficient lifestyle gradually gives way to a barter economy and in the end into a money driven one. To start with, the children will come up with a number of interesting considerations. It could be that a communist society will be pictured. Thus one child proposes that all people should take the goods they need. They would simply be available in the shops to freely pick and take. And there are a number of places in our society where something akin to this exists. In many families all members have free access to all victuals. If one is not supposed to take too much of a tidbit, this is not for financial but for health reasons. Yet in the overall societal context, nobody trusts people to have the needed self restraint. If people were perfect, yes—but . . . How on earth should one decide who needs a recreational vehicle and who a sailboat?

Other children go straight for barter. People get part of the goods they produce and barter this for what they need. For example, if someone works in a refrigerator factory, he gets two refrigerators at the end of the month. Imagine the required effort needed for such a person to buy a breakfast. His baker is amply supplied with refrigerators, yet those who may need refrigerators may not have baked goods to give away.

A good example in real life to speak about is the recent conditions in Eastern Europe where intensive barter trade developed along the radial streets around Moscow and in other places. For example, if someone needed two tires for his car, he had to be able to offer something of equal value. Perhaps a few bags of cement were still stored in his cellar from a time when a building was erected near his home. The cement is still usable, so it is brought to one of the places of barter. There another person is looking for cement to build something at his summer cottage. Unfortunately tires were desired in exchange for the cement. But the prospective buyer of the cement happens to have some boxes of cigarettes with him, which have roughly the same value of the cement. Quick figuring takes place. The owner of the cement thinks that he can retain a few packages of the cigarettes and still find his tires. So he takes the cigarettes for the cement knowing he can exchange them for the tires he needs. The cigarettes have some important advantages. Firstly they are much easier to carry around; secondly one can subdivide them into small portions by individual package (or even single cigarettes); thirdly cigarettes are wanted everywhere in Russia and are accepted even by non-smokers who can easily barter them. In the end the tire seeker finds a place of barter somewhere else and the desired tires will be exchanged for several cartons of cigarettes and can even retain a few packages.

This example provides much material for discussion, for one thing, the degree of effort barter involved in a society based on the division of labor. Then, too, one can observe the creation of money first hand. In 1990 one could still observe how packages of Western cigarettes went from hand to hand in a country in the Eastern bloc. Everyone was sure that he could easily get rid of them again and hardly anyone would even dream of opening them. If someone really wanted to smoke, he found dried-out cigarettes, often squashed by repeated handling. By *consuming* the cigarettes *as merchandise,* he would create a loss he would not have encountered had he continued to use them as objects of barter.

Here one may point out that in the above countries money did indeed exist, but the money was somehow diseased. We shall explain the nature of this disease later on.[21]

From barter one can go back to a self-sufficient life style. One speaks of a self-sufficient economy in which people provide all that is needed for themselves and their families. Such conditions were found in families, kinships, and small tribes among aboriginal peoples, such as the original inhabitants of Australia, Eskimo tribes, and similar groups. Since nature gives us the basics for our lives, such forms of economy are always strongly dependent on it. One still finds, right up to our own century, far reaching self-sufficiency on well-established farms. Division of labor is based on abilities and strengths, not monetary calculations. Every member gives the community what he has accomplished and takes what is given him or what he thinks he deserves.

Even though much discussion may be of hypothetical nature, the children can well describe what leads to barter and thus to the development of a barter-based economy. On one hand this is the existence of desired goods that are not available within one's own country or, on the other, things beyond one's abilities, such as building your own house or buying bananas in Norway.

If the work session succeeds to close the loop, at it were, at the first try, and to come back to the use of money in our present economy, then a connection between the birth of a money economy and the *division of labor* can be established. The division of labor creates more highly developed abilities, and these can in turn lead to more skillful work and better products. The division of labor makes people work for each other, yet it specializes them at the same time. The homework assignment can be a small written essay on the theme "The Usefulness of Money." A collection of catchwords or short sentences taken from the discussions may be helpful here.

Since on day one there is no discussion of homework and no papers are due, it is possible to have a refresher of a theme which may serve as preparation for coming days, namely *fractions*. It must be demonstrated that one can obtain half, a third, a quarter, and so forth, of a value by multiplying with the corresponding fractions. To do this one can start with a value of, for example, $6.00. The following sequence shows very clearly how it is possible to increase as well as decrease by multiplying.

$$
\begin{array}{rcccll}
3 & \times & \$6.00 & = & \$18.00 & \text{is three times} & \$6.00 \\
2 & \times & \$6.00 & = & \$12.00 & \text{is twice} & \$6.00 \\
1 & \times & \$6.00 & = & \$6.00 & \text{is once} & \$6.00 \\
\frac{1}{2} & \times & \$6.00 & = & \$3.00 & \text{is half of} & \$6.00 \\
\frac{1}{3} & \times & \$6.00 & = & \$2.00 & \text{is one third of} & \$6.00 \\
\frac{1}{10} & \times & \$6.00 & = & \$0.60 & \text{is one tenth of} & \$6.00 \\
\end{array}
$$

Once they grasp this, the children can calculate $\frac{1}{2}$, $\frac{1}{3}$, $\frac{1}{4}$, $\frac{1}{6}$, of $12.00. If the teacher feels it is appropriate, a few exercises may be given as homework. The important point is that it is understood that *multiplication* can be used to calculate fractions. It is best to do this with similar sequences.

To conclude the lesson a preview of the next day is presented, followed by an appropriate sixth grade tale.

Proposed Homework
1. Write a short essay on the theme "The Use of Money in the Economy" (see above).

2. Calculate
$$\frac{1}{2}, \frac{1}{3}, \frac{1}{4}, \frac{1}{6}, \frac{2}{8}, \frac{3}{12}, \frac{1}{24} \text{ of } \$24.00.$$

The Second Day
After the rhythmic part with recitations or musical exercises, mental arithmetic should be exercised. Sequences similar to those at the end of the last lesson may be used for this purpose.

Calculating percentages may also be added to this early activity because percentages are calculated in the same way as fractions—by multiplication, except here we always deal with the one hundredth part. In this way the systematic treatment to come is being prepared for by mental arithmetic.[22]

To start the working sessions it may be well to recall how humans work among themselves and that one has already learned about several forms of economy. The teacher can ask for the meanings of expressions like *self-sufficiency, barter economy,* and *money economy.* Some of the children will read aloud their short essays about money. Then the teacher asks, "Why are people who use barter economy usually better off than people who look only after themselves and their immediate families?" After arriving at a few ideas together the teacher can clarify the reason with a clear simplified example:[23]

Let us assume that two separate groups of people live on two islands in the Aegean Sea. Their principal source of food derives from fishing. But one of them has goats and produces goat cheese; the other, on the other island, has grapes and produces wine. Each island has a surplus of each product; on each, the other's product does not exist. Both islands are rich in a specific way. One has stores of cheese and the other of wine. But since both commodities spoil with time, they cannot increase their wealth by producing double the quantity. The excess would simply spoil and lose all its value.

Now, when people of both islands meet each other and exchange their goods, it suddenly makes sense to produce more wine and cheese than before because these can be exchanged. Both groups now have more merchandise than before—they have become wealthier. Now each island produces for the other one as well and become wealthier in the process.

What happens, however, if the people on the goat island start to cultivate wine themselves? One has to assume that now they can no longer exchange their cheese because they no longer need the wine of the other island. But because they have less experience in growing wine than the people on the other island, they will now have to drink poorer wine with their cheese. The people on the wine island will miss the cheese or try to produce it themselves. It gets poorer quality than the cheese they got from the cheese island. This need not remain this way forever, but it is often the case that when one party hopes to gain something by no longer needing the output of the other one, it results in a lessening of prosperity.

History shows many examples of such an island, spurred on by a few enterprising young people, waging war against the other one. They tried to get, for example, the cheese without having to surrender any wine. If they win the war, then the cheese producers lose their interest in producing good and plentiful cheese—after all, they no longer get wine in exchange. A scarcity of cheese develops on *both* islands, and the wine farmers are no longer able to dispose of their surplus of wine because the cheese was stolen and no longer paid for with wine. Winning the war helps only one party and only for a short time—until the robbed cheese has been consumed.

This is a way to discuss many questions. Examples abound in history up to our present time. These can be visited, even if the real situations are far more complex.

The basic question in every barter is: how much of one merchandise can be exchanged for the other? Both parties will have an interest to obtain as much as possible of the goods of the other one. Excepting the case where one item assumes a special value by means of other items as economic factors, it is a very important consideration how much of the goods are available and how much time is required to produce them. On Greek islands cheese and wine are consumed in moderate quantities, and the exchange will be felt to be equitable if the *time spent* to satisfy one party's needs is about the same as that to satisfy the other party. The facts that producing cheese is more uniform and that producing wine is very dependent on the season, are not relevant.

If the lesson is to go well, adequate thought must be directed at the central economic process of *establishing the price*. This establishes the correlation of reciprocal work. It is very appropriate here to be reminded of a southern market place where establishing the price is a careful game of taking each other's measure. Tourists from the north only too often fail to understand this, and it can happen to them that a seller lets the merchandise go below his own cost, tears up the money and throws it away. Such tourists know nothing about the balance that must be established in every sale (or barter). The southern merchant establishes a different price for each transaction; not the least of his considerations is the riches or poverty of the buyer. A good buy is only one where both parties have gained in the end. When selling too cheaply the producer of the goods is impoverished, when selling too expensively the goods may be left unsold. As a result of this the buyers cannot buy enough. They become paupers and, in the final analysis, the sellers do as well. This can never become a rigid relationship; it needs to be worked out in each case in a living manner. Over some time a balance of what both sides really need will establish itself unless some sort of the dominant conditions or externally enforced measures sneak in.

One could perhaps give the question of equitable barter as homework. Buying for money, too, is only a special form of barter. One gives money because one can do more with the merchandise than with the money. The merchant takes the money because he can do more with the money than with the merchandise. He thinks, for example, that with the money he can buy other goods of equal value as needed and pay for his upkeep at the same time. Part of the homework could be to have the children assess what in their surroundings they may be willing to exchange with each other.

For the time being a few arithmetical exercises with fractions or percentages should routinely be given.

Proposed Homework

1. Consider this question and write down some thoughts about it: Two people want to make an exchange. When will they both find the exchange to be just? Think of this based on the example of the Greek fishermen and on examples in your surroundings.

2. Calculate $\frac{1}{2}$, $\frac{1}{3}$, $\frac{2}{3}$, $\frac{1}{4}$, $\frac{2}{4}$, $\frac{3}{4}$ of 10 and 12.

3. Ask for a recipe for pancakes at home. Try to determine all ingredients by weight. (This homework can later be used for proportional percentages. The main reason for such definitions in hundredth parts lies in the fact that *quantitative comparison* between the percentile component part is much easier. How on earth could one bake a cake when it asked for $^3/_{51}$ flour, $^3/_{11}$ sugar, $^1/_{41}$ salt, and so forth? This would make it hard to visualize the component parts. But if one thinks of the whole as hundred and knows that the ingredients are $^{57}/_{100}$ flour, $^{15}/_{100}$ sugar, $^7/_{100}$ fat, $^{18}/_{100}$ fluid and $^3/_{100}$ other items, a student can quickly obtain a comprehensible picture of the quantitative *relations*. The advantage over absolute numbers—as they usually appear in cook books—lies in the fact that the relations are good for *every* quantity, whereas definitions in ounces are good only for a particular quantity.)

The Third Day

Following the rhythmic part, mental arithmetic with fractions and percentages continues. Then homework is being compared.

During the *work session* the children's written considerations on equitable exchange move the conversation back to the theme of the economy.

Now the hypothetical island situation should be broadened with one variation. Let us assume that on both islands one has become used to cheese and wine and wishes to have a regular supply. Soon the fishermen will no longer exchange the goods as a side activity on their way to sea. Often their fishing grounds lie far apart from each other. One fisherman separates himself and takes over the transport of the goods as they are needed between the islands. He carries not only his own cheese in his boat, but that of other producers as well. Additionally, he is not interested in who on the other side has filled each wine skin. He has become a *trader* and wishes that both sides feel that they get good service. This is because *his profit*—part of the goods—depends on the satisfaction of both sides of the interaction. Now the supply is no longer dependent on chance encounters; it becomes more regulated and the relationship of exchange of both goods becomes more uniform. The trader separates himself from the interests of one side and becomes a middleman between both groups.

Let us suppose that lust for adventure or a storm drives him off his usual path and leads him to a third island, where one grows corn and bakes bread. Suppose that both wine and cheese are unknown there and when sampled by the inhabitants, they find that they like them very much.

The business activities of the trader are now wider. He offers bread at the cheese island and on the wine island and is well accepted. Of course now more cheese and wine have to be produced for three islands. The bread island, too, is stimulated to greater activity. The economy prospers, and nobody can imagine how one could live only on fish and only one other product.

> *Economic prosperity is created when humans work for each other in such a way that their own work is gladly accepted by the other humans and when their own needs are being satisfied by the work of the other humans—when human beings work for each other in manifold ways.*

What about the question of the relationship of different goods to each other? In the past it was the task of the priests to fix the barter relationships of goods. In our modern economy we usually do not exchange goods but rather goods for money—we *buy*. It has been stated that this is also an exchange, only on one side we have money. In this way a *price* is created. What should be its magnitude? This question will have to be repeated often, and a simple answer is not possible. Steiner once stated, "A correct price exists when somebody gets a value in return for his product which enables him to satisfy his needs and naturally also the needs of those who depend on him until he has produced another identical product."[24]

Now we leave the island example and return once more to barter economy. In the previous barter transactions, cigarettes played a special part. Whoever accepted them was often not interested in smoking. It was important to him that they did not represent too great a value (as for instance a refrigerator might), that they could easily be transported, were readily accepted, and were available in sufficient quantities. At the same time there did not exist such an abundance that people lost interest. As long as they circulated as barter exchange the contents of the packages was even uninteresting. As stated, it was a good idea for smokers not to fail to inspect the contents. It was often better to simply keep on exchanging them. The broken cigarettes could not be smoked at all.

This shows what has to be asked of money. The note itself need not have any value, must not be too plentiful, but also not too rare, has to be accepted as a means of exchange within its own territory, be easy to carry around, it must be possible to divide and multiply it, and it must not be too easy to reproduce.

At the end of the work session an overview of the monetary system as it is practiced in most countries may be given. A good example is one's own country. In the United States the Federal Reserve Bank is responsible to regulate the money supply and credit, issue currency and manage the rate of exchange so that enough, but not too much money, is available. The government decides on the laws to regulate the monetary system, it prosecutes people who forge money, and it orders producers, dealers and sellers of services (this expression must be explained) to deliver goods and services against money. Thus money is a *legal document* with validity in the place where it is valid. This is evident when one tries to use foreign currency, such as Russian rubles, in another country. (Currency exchange is beyond our present scope.)

Before storytime the teacher can discuss the starting of a main lesson notebook and writing a few sentences for a short home essay on the theme: "What changes when traders take over the exchange of goods in a barter economy?" Catch words are: the trader must serve both sides well; he is located between the groups; supply gets more regular. The trader receives a livelihood from part of the goods he exchanges. He needs initial confidence in him (credit) when he undertakes his first journey because he cannot pay for his first load with different goods.

Proposal for Homework

1. Write a short essay on the theme: ""What changes if traders take over the exchange of goods in a barter economy?" (Give catch words, see above).

2. Calculate $\frac{1}{3}$ and $\frac{1}{7}$ of $10.00 ; $100.00 ; $1,000.00
   $20.00 ; $200.00 ; $2,000.00
   $16.00 ; $160.00 ; $1,600.00

Calculate the results to three places of decimals and round off to two places of decimals.

[Results *a*: $\frac{1}{3}$ of $10.00 = $3.33; of $100.00 = $33.33; of $1,000.00 = $333.33; of $20.00 = $6.67; of $200.00 = $66.67; of $2000.00 = $666.67; of $16.00 = $5.33; of $160.00 = $53.33; of $1,600.00 = $533.33

Results *b*: $\frac{1}{7}$ of $10.00 = $1.43; of $100.00 = $14.29; of $1,000 = $142.85; of $20.00 = $2.86; of $ 200.00 = $28.57 ; of $2,000.00 = $285.71]

3. Calculate 1%, 2%, 5%, of $150.00 and 126.21. Calculate the results to two places.
[Results: 1% of $150.00 = $1.50, of $126.21 = $1.26
2% of $150.00 = $3.00 , of $126.21 = $2.52
5% of $150.00 = $7.50 , of $126.21 = $6.31]

The Fourth Day

At the end of the rhythmic part, the arithmetic exercises with fractions are continued. When calculating interest it is also necessary to expand and reduce fractions. This can be reviewed orally or in writing. Exercises like the following should be included:

How many hundredths (%) are $\frac{10}{50}$? Answer: 20, because

$$\frac{2}{2} \times \frac{10}{50} = \frac{20}{100} = 20\%$$

Or: how many hundredths (%) are $\frac{3}{25}$?
Answer: 12, because

$$\frac{4}{4} \times \frac{3}{25} = \frac{12}{100} = 12\%$$

Or: How many percent are $\frac{7}{20}$?
Answer: 35%, because
$$\frac{5}{5} \times \frac{7}{20} = \frac{35}{100}$$

Exercises of the kind above may given as homework.

During the work session an important advance in the way humans work together and in balancing their output can now be discussed as follows:

Three friends—Robert, John and Henry—are in the process of building houses for their families. Since they are craftsmen themselves they do not leave everything to contractors but do much by themselves, Henry is a mason, Robert an electrician and John a carpenter. Each keeps a careful record of the hours he works for the others and how much they do for him. After awhile the following statement is found in Henry's book:[25]

Henry's accounting for Robert

Date	Hrs. for R.	Date	Hrs. from R.
5/3	5	5/3	5
5/4	14	5/4	10
5/5	7	5/5	5
5/7	10	5/6	10
5/12	12	5/12	7
5/13	12	5/13	12
5/14	9	5/14	10
5/20	11	5/15	11
. . .	. . .	. . .	. . .
. . .	. . .	. . .	. . .
Sum	80		70

As can be seen Henry has worked 10 hours more for Robert than Robert has for Henry.

Henry's accounting for John shows in the same manner that he has worked for him 100 hours, while John had worked for Henry 120 hours. Thus John has credit for 20 hours.

Robert's accounting shows that he worked for Henry for 70 hours, yet received 80 hours in return. Thus he has to work for 10 more hours. For John he worked 90 hours and received 80. Thus he should receive 10 hours.

John finds that he should work another 10 for Robert, yet receive 20 hours from Henry. (This results from the respective accountings.)

Finally the friends mutually take account of the hours that each one had worked for the others and what he had received. First, they account for each one:

To Work	To Receive
Henry for John 20 hrs.	John from Henry 20 hrs.
John for Robert 10 hrs	Robert from John 10 hrs.
Robert for Henry 10 hrs.	Henry from Robert 10 hrs.

At this time Robert is very busy in his profession, and he has really done all he could for his friends. He should work another 10 hours for Henry, but he is due 10 hours from John. He proposes that John work the hours for him for Henry, but John says, "I still get 20 hours from Henry. But never mind, I will simply get only 10 hours from him and we will be even."

How can the friends get a good overview of this accounting? First they draw a diagram with arrows to show who has to work for whom how many hours (Fig.1). Then Henry says to Robert, "I get 10 hour from you, but I have to work another 20 hours for John. Give the hours to John instead of to me, then I need to work only another 10 hours for John." Robert and John agree to this. This situation is shown in Fig. 2. Now John says to Robert, "I was supposed to work for you another 10 hours. We can count those against the 10 hours that you are supposed to give me for Henry. This makes the two of us even and Henry owes me 10 hours." (Fig. 3.)

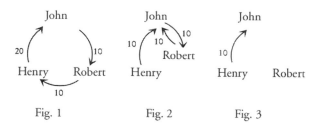

Fig. 1   Fig. 2   Fig. 3

What has been accomplished here? Initially 40 hours of time were owed under the two-sided accounting. By mutual accounting this is reduced to 10 hours! *By standing in for each other the community as a whole gains freedom. All that is needed is that we keep reliable notes of the demands and obligations and account for them.*

In addition we want to introduce *time accounts.* These are a great help in the settlement of accounts. They are tables with the times for each participant entered *twice,* once as work time performed *for* someone else and once as received work *from* someone else. This double entry insures that altogether the same number of demands as obligations are left over. The extra or outstanding performances must have their exact corresponding ones in one or several other accounts. Since only one amount of either more or less performed hours is shown for each person, the smallest possible number of hours to be accounted for is the result. In the line *sum* a separate addition is performed for each person. The line *difference* then indicates how much missing or excess time has been spent. Attention!!— If, as is the case with Henry, a difference is shown on the For-Side, he has not worked enough, if the difference is on the From-Side he still has credit for help! The last line is merely a control. If no mistake was made, right and left balance. In our example we obtain thus:

Settlement from Henry

For	Hours	From	Hours
Robert	80	Robert	70
John	100	John	120
Sum	180		190
Difference	10		–
Total	190		190

Settlement from Robert

For	Hours	From	Hours
Henry	70	Henry	80
John	90	John	80
Sum	160		160
Difference	0		0
Total	160		160

Settlement from John

For	Hours	From	Hours
Henry	120	Henry	100
Robert	80	Robert	90
Sum	200		190
Difference	0		10
Total	200		200

Again, all work done is entered twice, once as work performed and once as work received. One can see at once that Robert's account is balanced. As we have already seen in the figure, everyone has given and received the same if Henry works another 10 hours.

Let us go through another example. The friends enter the following hours into the diagram:

Settlement from Henry

For	Hours	From	Hours
Robert	70	Robert	90
John	110	John	50
Sum	180		140
Difference	0		40
Total	180		180

Settlement from Robert

For	Hours	From	Hours
Henry	90	Henry	70
John	75	John	80
Sum	165		150
Difference	0		15
Total	165		165

Settlement from John

For	Hours	From	Hours
Henry	50	Henry	110
Robert	80	Robert	75
Sum	130		185
Difference	55		0
Total	185		185

Here one can see that balance is established if John works an additional 40 hours for Henry and 15 hours for Robert.

These exercises should be thoroughly practiced, using different numbers and also given as homework.

Time Accounts—a Large Step Forward

The first type of settlements of accounts dealt exclusively with two-sided relations. Henry and Robert settled as though John had no part in it; Robert and John and John and Henry did the same thing. In this way one continues to deal with one's obligations to another person until the debt has been liquidated by work. The other persons have nothing to do with these obligations or still open demands. This is a barter trade economy wherein efforts are being exchanged with each other.

In the second method something quite new appears. The parties settle their demands *among themselves.* John can settle Robert's debts. The friends stand in for each other. In place of a demand on another person, a demand on the *community* has been created. One still requires something from the community, or one still has to perform something for it. The accurate depiction with numbers ensures that all is *justly* done.

This creates the beginning of *double entry bookkeeping.* Every event is entered twice in this way, once as work accomplished and once as work received. Once the number of hours is on the active side and once, with the receiver of the work, on the passive side. This resolution of mutual obligations represents a large step forward in that the individual gains *freedom* by it. He is no longer obligated and tied to one individual but to the community. He repays what he has received with different services and at freely arranged times. This discharge of individual obligations is usually done by payment. When I buy bread from a baker, I receive from him something he has done. By giving him money, I *disoblige* myself, and he can receive the compensation from a totally different source and choose *how* he is compensated. He can buy shoes, fill up his gas tank or go to the theater. I would not have been able to give him these compensations directly.

A report from England demonstrates that the compensation for time in its simplest form can be a currency. "The project unfolded in the community Kingston-upon-Thames and is called 'The Beacon.' The basic thought is the introduction of a new medium for payments next to the the state's pound sterling. Unit of payment is the 'beak' being issued by the communal CENTER FOR ENVIRONMENTAL CONCERNS. Its worth is defined as a unit of time of ten minutes. The most asked-for offerings are services, for example, painting and decorating, automobile repairs, courses in cooking, and so forth. The system is experiencing such a growth that the Bank of England already threatens to intervene."[26] It is understandable that this *secondary currency* presents problems because this stream of money creates nothing in taxes or social contributions for the community projects. Of course this also brings up the interesting question as to what degree unemployment is an artificial phenomenon, created by social and tax legislation. This is because it obviously there is enough work for them. We shall not address this question any further here.

The importance of communal accounting for work done and with it the creation of money is particularly clarified if one observes simpler older economic conditions.

In his biographical interview Bernard Lievegoed describes how such a social arrangement of simple conditions was found on the island of Java. "When it got dark we then went to some village and asked the Lura, the head of the place, whether we could sleep there. By the light of an oil lamp one got to hear endless stories about the harvest, the events in the village, and about who was poor and who rich. Richness implied something totally different than with us in the West. I still remember how I was told of a man who was very rich. I asked: Why rich? Does he have a lot of money? No, the man had no money. Did he own much land? No, of course he also had no real estate. Well, then, what did he have? The answer was: The man is rich because he is well connected.

"The Javanese word for 'rich' is hard to translate. I asked whether I could meet this man and I was taken to a small house next evening. The man sat on the floor and braided strips of bamboo he needed to repair his small house. I said to the Lura: now, what is so special about this man? The answer was, 'This man has helped many people!'

"Later on I understood what was meant. All who have helped other people are considered rich in Javanese society. Because, if one has helped many people one has the right to say to them: come, help me to repair my house; one time I have helped you also. If one makes use of that help the debt is paid. Yet if one allows the debt to remain one ends up having people all over the place whom one must help if they really need one. The Javanese go by the motto, 'The more one gives away the richer one becomes!'"[27]

One might also find similar conditions in the former communist countries. Everyone tries to have as big a network of acquaintances whom he could ask for services, be it repairing a faucet, obtaining foodstuffs that are hard to get, or similar circumstances. Such relationships are carefully nurtured by helping friends with something they are interested in such as, for instance, to be ready to baby sit in emergencies, or to lend one's tools. One was rich if one could call on many such services in case of need. In essence it was always a matter of such two-sided relationships.

Since working with time accounts must be practiced, there remain only the assignment of homework, some work on the main lesson book and—prior to story time—a preview of the next day.

Proposed Home Work

1. How many percent are $\frac{1}{10}$, $\frac{2}{10}$, $\frac{3}{10}$, $\frac{4}{40}$, $\frac{8}{40}$, $\frac{10}{40}$, $\frac{20}{40}$?

[Result: 10%, 20%, 30%, 10%, 20%, 25%, 50%]

2. Exercises from the chapter "Percent and promille calculations"

3. The three wives of Henry, Robert, and John of course help build the houses and their furnishings. Astrid is a tailor, Betty is a gardener, and Chris a painter. It works best if all three do not try to do all the work in her own house but if each one does what she is best at in all three houses. After some time the following numbers of hours result:

Astrid for Betty	170 hours	Betty for Astrid	150 hours
Astrid for Chris	30 hours	Chris for Astrid	90 hours
Betty for Chris	120 hours	Chris for Betty	90 hours

Enter the times in time accounts and calculate the outstanding work and demands.
[Result: Astrid still has to work 10 hours for Betty and Chris 30 hours for Betty.]

The Fifth Day

Toward the end of the first week of the main lesson, questions about money can be posed again and answered during the working session. After review of the homework the introductory example with Henry, Robert and John can be taken up again. The result was defined as the need for Henry to work 10 hours more for John. But Henry is a mason and the masonry work is completed. John is far more in need of a plumber. Henry offers himself but knows that this plumbing would not be very professional. He can accomplish more as a mason. He gives John the *amount of money* that would represent 10 hours of work, and he goes somewhere else to lay bricks which yields good wages for him. The plumber does not only do better work than Henry would, he also works faster, thus accomplishing many times what Henry could have done. In this way everyone is content: the plumber has found work, Henry does not need to relocate water pipes, and John knows that the work will be done professionally. Henry has paid his debt to John with the money. John can take the money and use it to engage another person who has the needed expertise.

Money fulfills obligations for the one who gives it and gives the recipient the ability to claim service from the economic community in which he lives.

Now it is possible to talk about additional concrete facts connected to our daily lives. For example, the teacher, by instructing the school class, renders a service for the parents, the children, and humanity as a whole. Yet, unlike past practice in the villages, the parents do not bring him potatoes, eggs, sausage, bread, and so forth, but he receives a *salary.* He can use this to buy the bread and all the other items. He works for one set of people and others work for him (the baker, the butcher, the worker in a factory).[28]

In summary the three forms of economy may be compared once again:

- Self-sufficient economy
- Barter economy
- Money economy

In a *self-sufficient economy* everyone works for himself and his dependents. This work is done primarily on nature, because nature nourishes and maintains our life.

In a *barter economy* goods are exchanged that in every case are worth more to the recipient than what he gave in exchange. However, work (services) can also be exchanged. In this manner, the fiddler at a wedding receives cake, sausages and bacon for his playing, without himself having given tangible merchandise. Yet in reality, cake, sausage and bacon exist only because someone has made them. Nature has contributed her part without charge.[29] Thus here, too, humans exchange their own work, performed at some time in their lives (exchange of life time).

In barter it is always necessary that goods and services of mutual interest meet. The example of the cement and the tires shows how difficult this can become under some circumstances. In this system much time and energy is lost. Division of labor, however, represents a great gain for both sides. Every person does what he can do better than the others and in this way all become wealthier.[30]

The two-sided relationships are resolved in a *money economy*. Money removes the recipient's obligation to render a service or a commodity and the economic community within which the money is valid steps in for him. Money gives us a claim for performance on the part of the *community with joint liability*. An economic community is a large community with joint liability. Within it money is a sort of *claim certificate* against services of other people. In the final analysis this means against some of their life time.

This may be compared to the introduction of *central perspective* at the beginning of modern times. With Giotto one can still find pictures where solitary objects are drawn in perspective but where no common perspective determines the direction of all lines. With the achievement of common perspective during the Renaissance, the geometry of each picture is oriented on the main point, the vanishing point of the lines as they reach vertically into the depth of the image. Yet this point indicates nothing other than the location of the eye of the observer. The entire picture is, as it were, oriented toward the latter's position. Similarly money gives us a claim on the society we live in. No relation to another human being, except ourselves, is immediately involved.

The modern monetary process differs from earlier forms of money and its usage in many respects. It is dependent on dual entry bookkeeping, a method which had its beginnings about five hundred years ago during the Renaissance.[31] Interestingly, historically this roughly coincides with the origin of common perspective.

According to the seventh year curriculum for the Waldorf schools, one should not forget to draw attention to these relationships in connection with history lessons depicting the beginnings of modern times. Modern age, with its consciousness soul[32] developments, announces itself, among other things with phenomena such as central perspective and dual entry bookkeeping. The start of an inner impulse of consciousness becomes apparent in the ordering of the way people work together. We laid the foundation for this earlier with the time accounts. The means of doing this may still be very cerebral, yet with the presentation in accounts it is possible to provide an overview of the total accomplishments of people who work together. This is part of the character of the sense-oriented consciousness soul.[33]

It is of course not possible to plan where the class discussions will lead over the course of a week. The described way is merely a possible example and suggests a few important topics.

I have also requested the establishment of time accounts for members of the child's family as homework (see below), in particular for the child himself. What does he give and what does he receive? When discussing the homework this resulted partly in rather embarrassed faces, but surprise over what certain ones have to do. This led itself to the questioning, which will be added as complement.

Complements

The settlement of times worked for each other, as we have done it in the time accounts, is the most elementary form of dual bookkeeping. Here life-time is the received magnitude. In many respects one can call it the most important one as well. What part of his life span has a person placed at my disposal, and how much do I place at the disposal of others? Yet the example of the three friends assumes that all three are equally efficient. How is one to proceed if in a community of coworkers one person can only accomplish little, perhaps for health reasons? In answer to this question the children come up with a whole list of proposals, such as: one credits him with only half the time.

One can indeed halve all the times of a person in the time accounts. Then he will have to work much longer than all the others. Obviously this is impossible in the long run because a person must sleep and the day has no more than 24 hours. This can create interesting conversations on the balance between justice and welfare. One could almost say that a classical quarrel between Capitalism and Socialism could erupt in the class. Next to the dictum, "He who does not work should also not eat," the feeling surfaces that "all human beings must live." If one has asked the children to consider their own time accounts, it is of course not very hard to get across the concept that in any larger crowd of people there must be some who cannot produce as well as healthy grownups. If the grownups considered only equivalent performances, no children could grow up and they themselves would have to be miserable in old age.

One can even continue with the question of whether one lives from one's pension in old age or from the work of the younger generation. In actual fact, one lives by the work of the younger people because one cannot eat money. In today's pension system an *entitlement* is created; yet experience shows clearly that the actual value of this entitlement is finally defined only when it is collected. The claim to live a life requiring one to cash in on previous savings is demonstrated by all children. They cannot live without donations. Grownups have no choice but to be *altruistic* vis-a-vis the children.

But there are other factors active in the mutual balance between working people beside willingness and the ability to work. Individuals' *abilities* are extraordinarily different. To receive one type of work from a particular person is not the same as to receive it from someone else. If one can listen to a good musician, one is willing to pay more than for a bad one. This is true in many areas. One person can only do work that many others can do for him as well. Another one is able to accomplish something that many would like to have him do for them. They express this with higher compensation (more pay). In this way very different levels of income can be created.

Here it is not a matter of evaluating these conditions in principle. The question of how one establishes a healthy relationship between performance and social justice is one of the most difficult ones for an economic community. Patentable solutions or social ideologies would not be very educational. Conversation that awakens consciousness in the children of the manifold aspects of the social question is more important.

Many a reader may think that these themes are too difficult for sixth graders. However it has been my experience that boys and girls of that age consider such thoughts of the human condition with the greatest interest. Among themselves, they bring the most varied points of view to life.

Thus one can experience directly how a social judgment can never be formed from only *one* way of looking at it. It is downright necessary to involve representatives of different justified agendas in the conversation. Perhaps a dynamic balance—which never remains stationary—can be found in this way. There is no such thing as ultimate social justice. It needs to be constantly explored. The history of the last century demonstrates to the interested teacher a sufficient number of cases which the observing social pathologist can describe as disturbances of balanced conditions.[34]

Proposed Homework

1. Establish time accounts for the members of your family and enter the times for everyone's activities for one week. Count only the times worked for each other!

2. A, B, C, and D work for each other and balance each other's time worked. After some time the following times result:

A for B 230	B for C 190	C for D 250	D for A 270
A for C 170	B for D 220	C for A 90	D for B 280
A for D 310	B for A 300	C for B 330	D for C 240

[Result: B still has to work 50 hours for A, 70 hours for C , and 10 hours for D]

3. Postulate times worked for each other among three friends. Balance them against each other. Cut the times worked by one of them in half and repeat the balancing operation. Compare the results.

4. Exercises from the chapter "Percent calculations."

The Second Week

Following the introductory discussions of different economic systems and money, the children may now be introduced to interest calculation in the second week. In order to do this one has to carry out the transition from *purchase money,* as discussed in the first week, to *capital.* This is the middle one of the three money processes; purchase money, borrowed money (capital), and gift money.[35] There is a connection between this and the creation of interest. Without understanding capital the creation of interest cannot be understood either. Although it is well known that one gets interest on deposits in a savings account, this in no way explains where the money comes from. If banks would always pay out more than they take in, they would soon have to give up. Therefore something must happen with the deposited money to enable the payment of interest. Again it is best to demonstrate this with a concrete case which contains the essential factors. The work of the second week can begin by relating such a case. From a pedagogical point of view I think it is important to start by speaking about *opportunities for work* afforded by loan money and not to start with the receipt of interest.

Mr. R and His Story

Mr. R had completed his apprenticeship as a cabinet maker at his local village and moved to a large city to look for work and to learn something new. He found what he was looking for at a small carpenter shop. He learned a considerable amount and finally was able to pass the master joiner test. He worked well with the master joiner who owned the shop.

The latter was already old and had to think about letting a younger man take over the shop. His daughter got on well with the new young master. They married and soon the young master took over the shop. The in-laws were taken care of for the rest of their lives. Now the young master could decide what he wanted to do for himself. He no longer wanted to make furniture; he wanted to produce something that could be sold in larger numbers. He developed modular exhibition walls, shelves and tables that could be quickly erected and taken down at trade shows and exhibitions. They were both good-looking and solid. The very first attempts at a trade show were a great success because at that time little comparable furniture of this type was available. In quick succession he received more orders than he could manage in his small workshop, limited to five workers.

It so happened that his father-in-law's small shop, built originally at the edge of the city, had long been surrounded by high-rise buildings and no longer fit into the the scene. The town offered him a site further out in an industrial area for a favorable price. What should he do?

One fine day Mr. R presented himself at his bank. This is the bank where he keeps his account, to which his customers pay their bills and from which he takes the money to buy wood, machines, materials, etc.[36]

He arranged a date when he met with the banker, armed with plans for a reorganization of his enterprise, along with the most important supporting documents.

This is a good place to start a conversation about what the children know that a bank does. They know about paying and receiving money, that they have a savings book with the bank and that there are ATMs (Automatic Teller Machines) where one can obtain money with a card. As a rule they are totally unaware of the fact that receiving and paying out money is by no means the most important activity of a bank. Now one can point out to them that every larger branch of a bank has, besides the room with the counters and tellers, one or more offices where one has the opportunity to discuss business transactions without being disturbed. Mr. R. will now engage in such a conversation. He does not have enough money to simply build a new place of business with machinery. The bank, however, could give him *credit* to do this.

On his part the banker has prepared himself for this conversation by checking whether R has made his payments punctually, how much money he has in his account, how much he has earned and spent, and much more.

He examines R's plans for the new building. Of course the cost is his main interest in this. R also shows him the large number of orders he has for his new display shelves. The banker investigates whether all that R is planning is really possible and asks several questions. Without R noticing this, at the same time a personal appraisal is taking place. He is being asked about his wife and children because it is known that men who have to take care of families are, as a rule, more trustworthy. They will not so easily give up on some effort, even when there are difficulties. At times it is even being investigated whether a person who applies for a loan is perhaps too fond of alcohol. One offers a drink again and again and if this is too eagerly accepted it makes a poor impression. The person in question may even fail to get the desired credit.

Each bank has its own methods for such personal appraisals; it must determine whether it can trust a person with other people's money. Therefore it tests first for *creditability* and secondly for *credit worthiness*. The word "credit" derives from the Latin "credere," meaning "believe." It means that every credit assumes *"trust,"* the trust of the credit-giver in the credit-recipient. Money made available in this manner is also called *loan money*. By the way, animals cannot make loans.

Since the conversation with R has been successful, a financing plan is worked out. This determines when, and how much, money is needed and when and at what rate R can start paying back.

Well, who has given R the money? It is the money people have deposited into the bank because they had no need for it at the moment and also, perhaps, the money of the children deposited into their savings accounts. Therefore, the money is not stored in the cellar of the bank, as some children imagine. It is passed on by the bankers to people who want to create something with it.[37]

Now R builds the new enterprise, he buys modern machinery, hires new help and is finally able to produce and sell his display shelves in adequate quantities.

At this point a simple discussion of the way R has to calculate his prices can take place. He must use the income to buy raw materials and pay wages, electricity, water, taxes and much else. He figures the price of his display shelves to allow for enough money to pay back the credit received from the bank as well. But because he creates values he can pay back more than what he had received from the bank. This "more" is the interest he pays the bank for loaning him the money as credit.

A sketch can summarize the process:

Saver	Bank	Recipient of credit	Buyer
saving money →deposit			
	deposits ——→credit		
		production ————→ goods	
		income ◄———— money	
	income ◄——— interest & repayments		
interest ◄——— income			

Should the bank keep the money of the savers in the cellar and later pay out more than it had received, the money would soon be used up and the bank would have to close. But R uses the money to create something that other people need and therefore buy. The price is designed to have him take in more than he spent. The savers who brought their money to the bank have enabled him to create his business, and they receive interest for this loan activity.

"You must imagine that your savings are put at the disposal of another person who is able to do something useful for all with the money. The bank, too, keeps part of the interest paid by R because people there need to live as well. They have to pay for the building and whatever belongs to the bank. What's left of the interest goes to the saver. If one stuffs one's money into a stocking, one really does nothing very useful with it because there are always people who could do something useful. But as a rule we know nothing about what somebody does with our money. Perhaps there are some things we would not like as much to support than others. For this reason there are banks which one can instruct for whom and for what the money can be used.

This conversation about Mr. R and the activity of banks may be concluded with this question: How should one determine the interest to be paid by the recipient of the credit (the debtor) or that due the saver who has entrusted the bank with his money?

Proposed Homework

Write a short essay about the activities of a bank and, particularly, about giving credit.

Arriving at the Formula for Interest

The next day it will be necessary to have a discussion in connection with the homework. This will deal with the totally different use of money in a case like Mr. R's, when compared to ordinary shopping. First of all R has used the money to erect the building and to buy new machines. These will be in use for a long time. If one buys a loaf of bread it is soon consumed, which cancels out its value as merchandise. Mr. R's building and machines do not serve consumption, rather they serve the production of goods. The machines' value decreases only slowly as a rule. In place of the value in money received by R from the bank, the building and machinery are available. At least to begin with, these represent a correspondingly equal value. This value can be expressed in money. Together with the available money it forms Mr. R's *capital*. This capital is now used to produce new values which generate interest. The capital has, for the most part, been created from loaned money. Thus, in essence, it is *loan capital*. One actually counts even what R already possessed—machines, money, and so forth—as capital which he has loaned to the enterprise.[38] He too expects that it will yield interest for him, which he can live on—even his successful activities yield interest, but not "automatically" as would be the case with a savings book. In fact, if this would not happen, it may be better if he were to give his own money to another concern which would pay interest. Thus it is correct to look at capital as loan money.

But how should one pay interest on capital given to an undertaking? The bank first gets interest from R. How does it go about distributing the appropriate part to the savers?

The conversation which follows this question confirms the truth of Steiner's indication "that the human being has an instinct for earning interest from what can be reaped. . . ."[39]

Discussions I have had in this connection have resulted in the following. The first proposal was that every saver gets the same amount. One pupil instantly had the thought to subdivide the money and to pay it to five or six different places. This made it obvious that the interest had to depend on the *amount* of the deposited money. The next variation was that everyone should receive a certain sum in keeping with his deposit. Right away one of the children sensed his advantage and said that, in this case, he would deposit his money, cash his interest and take the money out again in order to loan it out elsewhere for a short time. In this way he would make the most money. This brought in the question of *time*. The interest must depend on *how long* the money is made available for credit.

At this point the teacher can report that this is in fact what happens. One agrees on a *percentage* (interest rate), to be paid for *a full year* loan time. If the time is only half a year, the interest is only half, if it is quarter of a year there is a right to a quarter of the yearly interest, and so on.

Once this is determined one can do a lot of things. To practice the rule thus gained a number of interest calculations can be carried out orally or in writing. Assume a person has made $1,000 available to some undertaking. An interest rate of 10% has been agreed upon. How much money does the lender receive after a year? How much would he receive if he were to make the money available for only half a year? Then one can vary the rate of interest. In this way one can familiarize the children even during the first discussion with interest calculations. Corresponding home work should be assigned.

Suggestions for Homework

1. Determine interest for a capital loan of $1,000, $2,000, and $5,000 with an interest rate of 8%.

Show the interest for 1 year, $\frac{1}{2}$ year, 2 months = $\frac{1}{6}$ year.

Result:

t/C	$1,000.00	$2,000.00	$5,000.00
360	$80.00	$160.00	$400.00
180	$40.00	$80.00	$200.00
60	$13.33	$26.67	$66.67

2. How can a bank pay interest on savings accounts? Who actually pays the interest in the end? (The consumer who pays more or less for a commodity because the cost of capital is worked into the price of the goods.)

The Formula for Interest

The next day a decisive step must be made into the area of applicable laws. One does not start the day by reviewing the homework but reminds the children in a general way that the day before a just way of calculating interest had been discussed. Then one asks the class: Who can describe the law according to which interest is being calculated?

When I posed this question a number of children tried to start with numerical examples taken from the school lesson or the homework. I very quickly put a halt to this approach and asked again, more clearly: The law, the rule *how* interest is being calculated, is really the same in all cases. Can somebody describe this law without examples?

At first the question resulted in amazement. Yet it is extraordinarily interesting which of the children are actually able to formulate a law as conceptual relationship. When I dealt with this question for the first time in one class a girl answered. She was in no way an outstanding math student but often presented more deeply experienced and thought-out ideas in conversation. She said something like, "Well, one has capital; one loans it to somebody and agrees with him on a portion of it which he has to pay in interest after one year. One expresses this as a percentage. One calls it the interest rate. If the money is borrowed for less than one year, the interest is accordingly reduced."

Although this is as yet no formula, it contains all that is involved. The teacher should never create the feeling that such a conceptual description is too "abstract." Far from that, one has just expressed the *essential* that is addressed in every case. Yet the essential of a subject is never abstract; rather it bestows sense and meaning to the details! Grasping a purely mathematical law of relations represents the crossing of a dividing line—the dividing line between thinking tied to forming mental pictures and thinking in concepts. Without crossing this line in one's development it will hardly be possible, later in life, to follow the thoughts in books like Steiner's *The Philosophy of Freedom* or any presentation of spiritual themes.

Much depends now on working with this result in conversation, on turning it this way and that, perhaps on questioning it again, but above all on applying it. To do this one tries to make a start to express the law in a mathematical formula. This is done by repeating what had been said in written form.

$$\text{Interest} = \text{Capital} \cdot \frac{\text{Interest rate}}{100} \cdot \text{Part of the year}$$

The early exercises with multiplication of fractions during the first week focused on understanding the occurrence of multiplication.

Now they find application.

After this, the teacher works through each of the factors once more. There are rules that need to be observed. One of these is that only amounts rounded off bear interest. Above all else the way time is calculated must be discussed. How is one to express parts of the year? A year most often has 365 days. In every leap year it has 366 days. (Leap years are usually every four years, except at the turn of a century and again at the turn of a millennium.) However, the people in different countries who must work out interest have come to an practical agreement to facilitate their calculations. The shortest time for which interest is paid is a day. They look at one day as $\frac{1}{360}$ of the year. Thus for one day $\frac{1}{360}$ of the yearly interest is paid, for two days $\frac{2}{360}$ and so forth. But so that this goes into a year with 365 days each month is assigned 30 days. Thus one counts 30 days from January 10th to February 10th; 60 days from January 10th to March 10th, and so forth. Only in spans of less than a full month does one count the days according to the calendar. But if one counts all months as having 30 days the result is $12 \cdot 30 = 360$.[40]

1. Example. How many interest days are between March 15th and September 19th? A: 6 full months and 4 days, thus $6 \cdot 30 + 4 = 184$ days. The following is a practical way to present the calculation of interest days:

D (day)	M (month)		
19	9		End date
−15	−3		Start date
4	6		
4	6		$6 \cdot 30 + 4 = 184$

If the date of the start day is greater than the end date, it is increased by 30 and the date of the month reduced by 1.

2. Example. How many interest days are there from May 17th to September 4th? Here is how this is calculated:

D (day)	M (Month)		
34	8		End date
−17	−5		Start date
17	3		$3 \cdot 30 + 17 = 107$

Now the rule or the law applying to interest calculation can be written again in this way:

$$\text{Interest} = \text{Capital} \cdot \frac{\text{Interest rate}}{100} \cdot \frac{\text{number of days}}{360}$$

Finally one abbreviates with single letters:

Interest	= I
Capital	= C
Interest rate	= p (from the Latin word *pes* = foot)
Number of days	= d

This brings us to a formula for interest calculation:

$$I = \frac{C \cdot p \cdot d}{100 \cdot 360} \quad \text{(interest per day)}$$

This is the famous and important *interest formula*. If interest is to be figured for a full year, d = 360 and the formula is simplified to:

$$I = \frac{C \cdot p}{100} \quad \text{(interest per year)}$$

The teacher should develop as clear an understanding of this formula as possible. Its essential aspect is that it connects time to money.

The fact that human activities run in time gives reality to this connection. Capital that does not lead to the creation of values falls out of the economic process.

Much that determines the relationships between national economies is based on this interest formula. As an example one can think of the difficult North–South relationship. This is complicated, among other things, by the fact that money has flowed from north to south and mostly used as consumption money, yet the south paid interest on it as capital. However, one cannot charge interest against money which serves consumption in the way that a justified investment credit does. If I buy bread with loaned money on which I have to pay interest, then I really eat part of tomorrow's bread today. One eats, as Goethe says in *Faust*, "already (the) consumed bread."[41]

Here one can point to medieval laws of interest. These prohibit the collection of interest on consumption credit. Christians were allowed to loan corn or similar commodities for needed consumption but were not allowed to charge interest for it. When a trader performed mercantile transactions he was allowed to participate in the profit provided the party involved gave of their own money as mercantile capital for an undertaking. Historically only Jews, as non-Christians, were allowed to accept interest for consumption credit. Perhaps many a pogrom had some connection with indebtedness due to demands for consumption credits. In any case the children should clearly understand the consequences of all consumption credit. The goods get more expensive for the consumer and, all in all, he has less money available for consumption.

Anybody who has experienced indebtedness on the part of young families knows how much harm consumption debts can create. It is important that the children understand the difference between an investment and a consumption credit very clearly and what significance each type has in life. The first releases human activities and leads to the creation of values, the second altogether reduces the ability to consume on part of the recipient of the credit. Preempted consumption of goods altogether reduces future possibilities. Simply put, if I buy fish with borrowed money, I will have fewer and fewer fish to eat in the future. If I buy a fishing rod with borrowed money, I might fish more than I need for myself, sell fish to others and in this way pay for the fishing rod and the interest. Of course each situation needs to be considered on its own merits. Even a private purchase on credit can be eminently sensible if it creates savings in another area.

One should also be conscious of the fact that banks do no make their profit from those who bring them their money, but from those who take out loans, to whom in fact they *give* money. This may well be the reason that often people receive credit, even though their ability to pay back is, in real fact, improbable.[42]

In the first place, the interest formula must be shown to be a concrete fact and seen in context with the global life of society. The questions indicated are therefore not to be understood as the content of a one-time presentation. They can be gradually touched upon as appropriate.

In order to help show the concrete reality of the formula one can return once more to the written calculations of the examples. The creation of a small *tabulation* is recommended as a start. Here the values of the various factors are listed. For example, the following tabulation records a case where the interest for a capital of $1,000 which is to yield interest at 8% p.a. (percent p.a. = pro anno = per year) and where the capital is being loaned for 180 days:

$$C = \$1,000$$

$$p = 8$$

$$d = 180$$

$$I = ?$$

The values are inserted into the formula, thus:

$$I = \frac{\$1,000 \cdot 8 \cdot 180}{100 \cdot 360}$$

As an automatic habit such an expression must first be *reduced, if possible.* In our example one obtains:

$$I = \frac{\$1,000 \cdot 8 \cdot 180}{100 \cdot 360} = \$40$$

This precise insertion of the values, reducing, and calculating must now be practiced with many examples. A formula that fails to help to determine individual cases quickly and reliably is useless. The children must experience the help the formula provides in calculating.

Then one can proceed from easily surveyed simple numbers to random ones. In particular one needs to progress from listing the number of days to working with dates.

Example:
Mrs. Cramer deposits $16,500 at 5% on March 15. On September 19 she needs the money to buy a used car. How much money is available for her?

Solution:

$$C = \$ 16,500$$

$$p = 5\%$$

$$d = ?$$

$$I = ?$$

The number of interest days is calculated $= 184$.

Inserted in the interest formula we get:

$$I = \frac{\$16,500 \cdot 5 \cdot 184}{100 \cdot 360}$$

$$I = \$421.67$$

Thus Mrs. Cramer has at her disposal $16,500 + $421.67 = $ 16,921.67

It will take some time to acquire ease in using such a formula. It needs thorough iteration in dealing with fractions, in particular reducing.

Consumption Money, Loan Money, Free Money

Parallel to the interest formula, meaningful conversation during lessons can deepen much of the subjects of the first week. For example, one can point out that the growth of Mr. R's furniture business had been, in essence, due to his invention of new display shelves. Without his expanding idea the undertaking would have been quite unnecessary and this lack would have resulted in ending the small firm. However inventions and ideas in many areas have a way of "wearing out." If new furniture finds acceptance, other people too will think about ways to make it easier and faster to assemble and disassemble and perhaps more beautiful. Customers will then go to a different manufacturer. Additionally, somebody could find ways to make the product cheaper and simpler. This too would present problems for Mr. R. Therefore, he is forced to not stop with one idea but to keep finding new ideas and improvements. One could almost say that ideas are for the economy what fuel is for the automobile. Both cease to move without new fuel. It is one of the tasks of education to train inventive and creative human beings. Eurythmy, handiwork, musical instrument, sports, and so forth, improve physical coordination. Coordinated limbs create flexible thinking. This can help make one a competent person.

These lessons provide a basis for an understating of the economic significance of the spiritual life. It is by no means unimportant for a national economy *how much* it invests in the education of growing generations and *how* it teaches them. Recent experience with, often well intended, developmental aid has amply demonstrated that all material help is of no value in the long run unless it enables independent creativity paired with a learning process aimed at helping oneself.

Observations like these can lead to the third form of the money process or type of money, namely to a way of using money that gives others the chance to live and grow without expecting any return. Giving another person something of one's own of which one had been able to dispose and renouncing one's rights is called *making a gift*. We refer to this as *gift money*. It performs an important task among human beings alongside consumption and loan money.

What is the best way to finance a school? The pupils receive an education there, yet they cannot themselves finance the teacher. The parents or other people must provide the money. Can it be looked upon as loan money? If one thinks in terms of long time intervals, all expenses incurred for education are an investment. But it takes about thirty years to take effect. To attempt to calculate something over this span of time is very uncertain. It is much better to *make a gift* of education to the young people. It is a process akin to sowing. The corn perishes so that new life can arise. In the same way people donate money so that new abilities can arise in young people.

It is also not too soon to make the children aware of the fact that education is not a process to be looked at primarily from an economic point of view. What happens between educators and children is centered on human issues. By their very nature these cannot be described with numbers—even though economic affairs play a role in many ways.

Such a conversation can reveal that a large number of human activities do not lend themselves to direct planning and calculation, or else they get corrupted and demeaned when captured with numbers. The creators of great works of art, those who research the basis of modern technological development, all those men and women contribute to the development of mankind with no possibility of calculating the effect in advance. They receive gifts of money and give the freedom to create what nobody predicted and nobody could, as yet, know.

Conversations like this can awaken a feeling for how necessary giving is for human life. Since the phrase "making a gift" has a connotation of useless things, good only to satisfy cravings, it may be better to choose the words *free money* because such money *frees* people to act creatively.

Summarizing one can once more alert the children to the character of the three money processes:

- I use consumption money to fill my needs.
- I use loan money to enable someone else to start an activity, yet I reserve a gain or even some say over it for myself.
- I use gift or free money so that another can live and grow without imposing conditions. The most fruitful human accomplishments have been created with such gifts.[43]

Nowadays such creations are being financed, among other ways, by taxes. As opposed to gift money, here the intentional gesture of the giver is lacking. Not only do taxes make it possible to educate, research and work artistically, but a community can also perform tasks impossible for single individuals to accomplish, for example the maintenance of police forces, building of roads, and more. This may be a good occasion to point out that community tasks may be financed in many ways and that the state imposition of taxes is not the best way for all purposes.

It it is possible that the conversation with the children will take quite different directions. Yet, as already mentioned, the economic importance of a free life of the spirit should start to resound here in a simple manner. This is the most immediate topic to tackle, beyond the three forms of money. This should not reduce the life of the spirit in the wrong way to matters of money. However, the damaging misunderstanding should be avoided that the life of the spirit has no economic implications for the life of a human community. It is terrifying to what a degree inappropriate education, ridicule and suppression of spiritual life can cause social sickness in our times. An education aimed at production rather than at creativity will, in the long run, ruin a national economy. The limitation to only materially useful items will lame the verve to create new ideas.

In his book *World Economy* Steiner points out that a dangerous blockage in the flow of money takes place if gift money is insufficient. In such a situation instead of the creation of abilities, speculative investments of money are created. These create fake values. They make no economical sense and are devastating in their social effects.[44]

Practice Exercises
Group 1: Calculating Interest
1. Calculate interest I on a credit C with an interest rate p, payable at the indicated time.

C	p	Interest time	d	I
$300.00	10	3/21 to 5/21		
$500.00	12	3/21 to 5/28		
$7,000.00	12	3/21 to 6/4		
$3,600.00	12	4/1 to 12/9		
$4,800.00	14	4/21 to 8/7		
$7,200.00	14	4/21 to 8/7		
$12,723.00	14.5	3/6 to 12/12		

2. Work through the exercise and its solution:

A machine, costing $24,000.00 is behind financed with credit. The interest rate is 12%. The purchase is conducted on March 3rd. On May 1st $12,000.00 of the loan is paid back. The remainder, including interest, is to be paid back on August 1st. How much is to be paid?

First we calculate interest I_1 and I_2. These have to be paid for both periods.

$$I_1 = \frac{\$24,000 \cdot 12 \cdot 60}{100 \cdot 360} = \$480.00$$

$$I_2 = \frac{\$12,000 \cdot 12 \cdot 90}{100 \cdot 360} = \$360.00$$

$$\text{Remaining payment} = \$12,000 + I_1 + I_2$$
$$= \$12,840$$

3. Solve the exercises in this table, in accordance with the preceding one:

Machine Price $	Interest Rate %	Purchase Date	Date 1st Payment	Amount 1st Payment	$ still owed	Date due	I_1	I_2	Amount remaining payment
$20,000	10	3/3	5/3	10,000		8/3			
$36,000	12	3/3	6/3	12,000		10/3			
$120,000	12	3/3	6/5	50,000		12/10			
$24,000	11	5/2	5/28	18,000		9/30			

4. Work through the following exercise to its solution:

A machine costs $100,000. It is being paid for in annual installments within 5 years. With each installment repayment of $20,000 plus the accrued interest is being paid. The rate of interest is 12%. Figure out the amounts of each installment. What was the total of payments for the machine?

Solution:

First installment: at the end of the first year a $20,000 repayment and 12% interest on $100,000 have to be paid.

This is $^{12}/_{100}$ • 100,000 = $12,000

The first installment then amounts to 20,000 + 12,000 = $32,000

Second installment: At the end of the second year $20,000 repayment and 12% interest on $80,000 are due.

This amounts to $^{12}/_{100}$ • $80,000 = $9,600.

The second installment then is $20,000 + $9,600 = $29,600.

The third installment: apart from the $20,000 repayment, interest on $60,000 must be paid. That is $^{12}/_{100}$ • $60,000 = $7,200.

The third installment then is $20,000 + $7,200 = $27,200.

The fourth installment: interest on 40,000 must be paid. That is $^{12}/_{100}$ • $40,000 = $4,800.

The fourth installment then is $20,000 + $4,800 = $24,800.

Fifth installment: interest must be paid on the remaining 20,000. That is $^{12}/_{100}$ • $20,000 = $2,400.

The fifth installment then is $20,000 + $2,400 = $22,400.

In all:

1. Installment	$32,000
2. Installment	$29,600
3. Installment	$27,200
4. Installment	$24,800
5. Installment	$22,400
Total	$136,000

Frequently such installments are being equalized. In this case the yearly payments are:

$136,000 : 5 = $27,200

Such payments are understood to include all interest in all payments but not the full amount of repayment at the beginning. Thus one pays more interest at the beginning and at the end, more repayment. In actual practice such payment and interest agreements can be even more complicated.

5. Using the model of the example, calculate the installments for a cost of the machine of $120,000 and 9% interest when the debt is paid back in 6 years.

The Beginning of Algebra

One can use assignments similar to the following to move toward algebraic conversions. In the United States parents have to pay very high fees so that their children can go to a good university. A well to do father decides to finance such studies by investing some money. He estimates that the university (tuition and living expenses) will require $30,000 a year. A friend of his owns a printing business and urgently needs a new machine. At the time interest on credit is 10% but interest on deposits only 6%. The two friends agree that the father shall partly finance the (very expensive) machine. He will invest enough to make the yearly interest amount to $30,000. They agree on an interest rate of 8%. In this way both enjoy an advantage. What is the amount of capital to make this sum available as yearly interest?

Let us try to solve this question using our interest formula as far as possible:

$$I = \frac{C \cdot P}{100}$$

The numbers are:

$$C = ?$$
$$p = 8$$
$$I = \$30,000$$

If we put these into the interest formula we have:

$$\$30,000 = \frac{C \cdot 8}{100}$$

This is the place we need the first algebraic conversion: what is the size of the capital if $\frac{8}{100}$ of it is $30,000?

To start with one can look for an improvised solution. For instance the children can argue:

If $\frac{8}{100}$ of the capital is $30,000 then $\frac{1}{100}$ of it is $\frac{1}{8}$ of $30,000, thus $3,750. This is $\frac{1}{100}$ of the capital we are looking for. The capital is then 100 times that, namely $375,000.

This conversation covers a specific case, only just within reach of the best pupils. One can commend them highly for this and say that: this solution contains laws and we shall now proceed to work these out step by step.

To better prepare ourselves for this we start to work through a number of simple problems. We solve these first verbally and then in writing. Writing involves showing the problem with the aid of letters. We start to use letters for as yet unknown numbers.

Examples:

8 is twice a number we pick. What number have we picked? (4). Writing it out, if we name the given number a, the exercise looks as follows: $8 = 2 \cdot a$. The solution is: $a = 4$.

51 is three times a given number. What number was given? (17) Written out the exercise is: $51 = 3 \cdot b$. Our answer is: $b = 17$.

82 is 41 times a given number. What number was given? (2) Written out the exercise is: $82 = 41 \cdot c$. Our result is: $c = 2$.

Of course one can express the exercise in reverse as well:
Five times a given number is 45. What number was given?

Written: $5 \cdot d = 45$; $d = 9$

This needs to be practiced until the oral exercise ares put into written form reliably. A page of such exercises can be given for homework.

The next day algebraic conversions can be used to arrive at a law. The aim is to establish the purely conceptual articulation of the relation between problem and solution. One can say something like: First a number is given. We know that this is so and so many times another, unknown, number. We name this unknown with a letter. How then do we find the unknown number? Gradually the children will find out that they have to divide the first given number by the multiplier (*so and so many times*) of the unknown number in order to find the latter.

I begin illustrating this law by symbolizing it with *colors* or different forms, where each color or form stood for a specific number. Of course it is hard to write such colors or forms and one cannot give them names as well if one needs too many different forms. This is the reason why one uses *letters* in this case, although letters have little to do with calculating.

One can express the applicable law in these words:

If a number is the product of a second and a third one, then the third one equals the first one divided by the second one.

Expressing this in letters we get:

If a,b,c are random numbers where
a = b • c
then it is always true that:
c = a/b

Whereas one *multiplies* when defining the problem, one *divides* when solving it.

The relation found between the definition of the problem and its solution is, thus, a general law like the interest formula. However the latter has been agreed upon between human beings, because it seems to be just. The mathematical law is not subject to be agreed upon one way or another.

In this way we begin *algebra*. Algebra teaches us to express and apply general laws that exist between numbers and, by using these laws, to convert these expressions. One often uses letters to express conformity to some law in algebra, as we have already done with the interest formula. In most cases the letters represent some particular number. However it is an important rule that the same letter in the same context should always express the same number. Yet two different letters can possibly express the same number.

Like the day before one can now present a group of exercises where one divides instead of multiplying. The problems will then be of the following type:

Examples:
The third part of a given number is 8. What number did I have in mind? (24).
Written it is: $8 = a/3$. The solution is: a = 24.

Turned around the exercises have this form:
The seventh of a given number is 5. What number have I picked? (35)
Written this is: $b/7 = 5$; b = 35

Now one can put the law into words:

If a number divided by a second one produces a third one, then
the first one equals the product of the second and third ones.

In letters this means: if $^a/b = c$, then $a = b \cdot c$.

For instance if we choose
$\quad$ a = 12, b = 3, c = 4, then $^{12}\!/_4 = 3$; and at the same time $12 = 3 \cdot 4$.

One needs to emphasize very strongly that every law, once found is immediately made very real by examples.

$\quad$ Then too we need to point out to the class that in the exercise we *multiplied* first, but *divided* to find the solution.

$\quad$ Once the law is established it is practiced with a number of problems. In the process the children must become aware that the letters used are of no importance, we only need some sort of *bookmark* to remind us that at that place one needs to think of a number. The *reason* for the rules that have been discussed is to find a number, as yet unknown, which is part of a multiplication or division.

$\quad$ The focus of the teaching of *equations* is to peel unknown numbers out of mathematical calculations. By making our starting point the interest formula we have so far arrived at the encapsulation in multiplications and divisions. Later in this teaching we shall have to solve additions and subtractions as well. Although the actual teaching of equations must wait for the seventh year of school, relevant subjects may be woven into the lessons already at this point. For example: I think of a number, reduce it by 7 and obtain 11. What number had I picked? The answer is 18, because $18 - 7 = 11$ or $18 = 11 + 7$.
We go no further with these preparatory exercises but turn to the third rule so as to stay within our context.

$\quad$ Again we can start with oral and written exercises. Now it will be a matter of finding the unknown denominator of a fraction in the way we found the numerator before.

The following are examples for such exercises:
$\quad$ 12 divided by a picked number makes 3. What number was picked? (4) $\quad$ Written: $12 \div a = 3$; $a = 4$.
$\quad$ 60 divided by a picked number makes 15. What is the picked number? (4) $\quad$ Written: $60 \div b = 15$; $b = 4$.

$\quad$ What is 60 divided by if the result is 5? (12) Written: $60 \div c = 5$; $c = 12$.

After solving some such exercises together, written ones should be done. For example:

$$6 \div u = 2; \quad 7 = 49 \div v; \quad 10 \div r = 0.5, \text{ and so forth.}$$

Once the relationship has been sufficiently practiced, the governing law may be formulated. It is:

$$\text{if } \tfrac{a}{b} = c, \text{ then } b = \tfrac{a}{c}$$

In conclusion the three laws should be placed side by side and summarized thusly:

In letters:

$$\tfrac{a}{b} = c, \quad a = b \cdot c, \quad \tfrac{a}{c} = b \text{ are all correct (or wrong) at the same time.}$$

Now these relationships need to be practiced in parallel in many ways. Gradually simple and decimal fractions should be introduced.

Practice Exercises
Group 2: Algebraic Conversions

1) $\tfrac{C}{7} = 5$ 2) $\tfrac{C}{100} = 3$ 3) $\tfrac{C}{30} = 1$ 4) $\tfrac{C}{100} = 0.1$

5) $\tfrac{r}{6} = 1/2$ 6) $\tfrac{S}{4} = 1/4$ 7) $\tfrac{25}{x} = 5$ 8) $\tfrac{24}{x} = 4$

9) $\tfrac{20}{d} = 2$ 10) $\tfrac{3}{r} = \tfrac{1}{2}$ 11) $\tfrac{10}{y} = 0.1$ 12) $4r = 12$

13) $4u = 10$ 14) $4v = 11$ 15) $7v = 14$ 16) $7v = 13$

17) $3w = \tfrac{6}{11}$ 18) $3w = \tfrac{5}{11}$ 19) $17w = \tfrac{51}{9}$ 20) $0.1a = 0.5$

Once this type of conversion is mastered, expressions with a number of letters should also be converted.

Practice Exercises
Group 3: Algebraic Conversions

Convert to show value of indicated letter:
1) $u = \frac{7}{v}$ $v = ?$ 2) $u \cdot v = 7$, $u = ?$ 3) $x = \frac{13}{y}$, $y = ?$

4) $x \cdot y = 13$, $x = ?$ 5) $2u = 7v$, $v = ?$ 6) $\frac{20}{t} = 2x$, $t = ?$

7) $\frac{20}{d} = 2x$, $x = ?$ 8) $81r = 192t$, $r = ?$ 9) $17ab = 119b$, $a = ?$

Conversions and examples
      The conversions practiced earlier should be taken up and discussed anew another day. This time we do not focus on the fact that one equation results in another one, but the thought needs to be brought up that equations can be *converted* by performing the same multiplication or division on both sides. This points to a fundamental principle that enables new and correct answers to be obtained from algebraic expressions:

> *If properly handled and under certain conditions the application of the same operation on both sides of an equation again produces correct results. In short: one is allowed to do the same thing on both sides of an equation.*

Using the form we have used until now the rule sounds as follows:

> *We are allowed to multiply with the same number and divide by the same number on both sides of an equation. (Division by zero is not allowed.)*

      Now we are dealing with the first beginnings of algebra. Once more we start with elementary examples, but we interpret their solutions in a new way.

First Example:
The number represented by a letter is to be worked out in the following example:

$$18 = 3 \cdot a$$

Solution: If we divide both sides by 3, we obtain on the left side
18 : 3 = 6, and on the right side 3a : 3 = a.

If we think of the equal sign as the beam of a scale, we could also describe the process of solving the equation thus: If the two sides, namely "18" and "3 • a" are in balance, then balance must exist if we take only a third of each side, that is if we divide 18 by 3 and also divide "3 • a" by 3 we get 6 = a or a = 6.

The new thought arises here that one may divide both the left and right sides of an equal sign by the same number. But we may also multiply both sides by the same number, as well.

Second Example:
Determine the number named b from the following relationship:

$$12 = \frac{b}{3}$$

Expressed in words this problem asks us to determine the original number that when divided by 3 results in 12. The solution is obviously b = 36, because a third of 36 is 12. We proceed systematically as follows:
We multiply on both sides of the equal sign with 3.
Thus we obtain on the left 12 • 3 = 36 and on the right $\frac{b}{3}$ • 3 = b; thus 36 = b or b = 36.

Third Example:
Given the expression $4 = \frac{20}{c}$ determine c. Since the numbers are easy to grasp we see that c = 5, because $\frac{20}{5} = 4$. But we can work out this problem also if we multiply both sides by c. Thus, 4c = 20 , and c = 5.

Such conversions are of the greatest importance in mathematics. We purposely chose our examples to be simple so that the answers are obvious. But, if we failed to apply these algebraic conversions we would not get very far in more complicated cases.

Let us apply our new knowledge to a few more examples of problems connected with real life situations.

Fourth Example:

A father wants to distribute $210 among his 5 children. What does each child get?

Solution: Let us express the amount received by each child as "a" then:

$$5 \cdot a = \$210$$

Let us divide both sides by 5 and we get: a = $42

Fifth Example:

6.5 ft. of cloth costs $72. What is the price of 1 ft.?

Solution: If we call the cost of 1 ft. of material "c," then: 6.5 c = $72. If we divide both sides by 6.5 we get: c = $72 ÷ 6.5 = $11.08 (rounded to two decimal places).

After a sufficient number of examples we can express the procedure as a rule.

> *If a number—whether known or unknown—is in the numerator on one side of an equation and is to be removed, then both sides must be multiplied by this number. If a number is in the denominator and is to be removed, then one has to divide both sides by this number.*

This rule applies also to cases where several letters or numbers are tied together by multiplications or divisions. This has already been pointed out in one of the groups of exercises, which gave the challenge to more advanced pupils to deal with a new level of problems on their own. Now we have a usable tool which anybody can use. But this requires practice.

Sample exercise:

Find unknown number a: $12 = \dfrac{3 \cdot a}{4}$ a = ?

Solution: First we multiply both sides by 4. This gives us:

$$12 \cdot 4 = \frac{3 \cdot a \cdot 4}{4}$$

We can shorten the 4 on the right $12 \cdot 4 = 3a$

Now we divide both sides by 3: $\dfrac{12 \cdot 4}{3} = \dfrac{3 \cdot a}{3}$

We get: $\dfrac{12 \cdot 4}{3} = 4 \cdot 4 = a, \quad a = 16$

To check our solution, we can substitute 16 for "a" in the original equation:

$$12 = \dfrac{3 \cdot 16}{4} = 12$$

Practice Exercises
Group 4: Algebraic Conversions

Find the numbers for each:

1) $18 = \dfrac{6a}{5}$, a = ?   2) $21 = \dfrac{3b}{5}$, b = ?   3) $28 = \dfrac{2c}{3}$, c = ?

4) $29 = \dfrac{2d}{3}$, d = ?   5) $27 = \dfrac{3e}{2}$, e = ?   6) $28 = \dfrac{3f}{2}$, f = ?

7) $2 = \dfrac{7g}{4}$, g = ?   8) $3 = \dfrac{3h}{5}$, h = ?   9) $2 = \dfrac{4i}{3}$, i = ?

10) $1 = \dfrac{2j}{3}$, j = ?   11) $\dfrac{3}{2} = \dfrac{2}{3}k$, k = ?   12) $\dfrac{2}{3} = \dfrac{2}{3}L$, L = ?

Group 5: Algebraic Conversions

Now we can work problems involving more letters. Solve for the letters, reducing as much as possible:

1) $u = 3v$, v = ?   2) $t = 2r$, r = ?   3) $x = \dfrac{y}{2}$, y = ?

4) $5 = \dfrac{u}{v}$, u = ?, v = ?   5) $2x = y$, x = ?

6) $x = \dfrac{3w}{r}$, w = ?, r = ?   7) $x = \dfrac{3w \cdot u}{2r}$, w = ? u = ? r = ?

Solve for each letter:
8) $a \cdot b = c \cdot d$,   a = ?, b = ?, c = ?, d = ?
9) $a \cdot b \cdot c = x \cdot y \cdot z$ a = ?, b = ?, c = ?, x = ?, y = ?, z = ?

Great care should be taken to record and work through each step. The only way to arrive at secure consistency in algebra is through the consistent practice of every step. One can compare these purely algebraic exercises with practicing scales and playing etudes in music. The are not carried out primarily for their own sake but in order to hone one's skills.

Practice Exercises
Group 6: Algebraic Conversions
Find the numbers indicated by the letters. Check each answer by inserting the result in the original equation.

1) $12 = 4a$ $\quad\quad 36 = 12b$ $\quad\quad 72 = 18c$ $\quad\quad 50 = 2d$
$\quad 720 = 180e$ $\quad 7200 = 1800f$ $\quad 171 = 19g$ $\quad 2363 = 17h$

2) $2 = 4a$ $\quad\quad 3 = 6b$ $\quad\quad 4 = 8c$ $\quad\quad 3 = 9d$
$\quad 6 = 9e$ $\quad\quad 12 = 8f$ $\quad\quad 16 = 12g$ $\quad 32 = 28h$

3) $\quad 7 = 2a$ $\quad\quad 13 = 7b$ $\quad\quad 51 = 17c$ $\quad\quad 64 = 48d$
$\quad 120 = 96e$ $\quad 1024 = 512f$ $\quad 896 = 56g$ $\quad 1 = 7h$

4) $\dfrac{1}{7} = 2a$ $\quad\quad \dfrac{2}{7} = 2b$ $\quad\quad \dfrac{3}{7} = 2c$ $\quad\quad \dfrac{4}{7} = 2d$

$\quad \dfrac{6}{7} = 3e$ $\quad\quad \dfrac{9}{7} = 3f$ $\quad\quad \dfrac{12}{7} = 3g$ $\quad\quad \dfrac{13}{5} = 3h$

5) $1 = \dfrac{1}{2}a$ $\quad\quad 2 = \dfrac{1}{2}b$ $\quad\quad 3 = \dfrac{1}{2}c$ $\quad\quad 3 = \dfrac{1}{3}d$

$\quad 5 = \dfrac{1}{6}f$ $\quad\quad 17 = \dfrac{1}{8}g$ $\quad\quad 2 = \dfrac{1}{23}h$

6) $3a = 0.6$ $\quad\quad 4b = 2.8$ $\quad\quad 5c = 3.5$ $\quad\quad 5d = 3.55$
$\quad 5e = 35.5$ $\quad\quad 7f = 0.49$ $\quad\quad 7g = 4.9$ $\quad\quad 7h = 49$

7) $5a = \$18.25$ $\quad 4b = \$24.16$ $\quad 4c = \$16.04$ $\quad 8d = \$17.20$
$\quad 3.6 \cdot e = \$84.24$ $\quad\quad\quad\quad\quad 4.8 \cdot f = \$1,202.88$
$\quad 7.7 \cdot g = \$10,073.91$ $\quad\quad\quad 9.11 \cdot h = \$63.77$

Back to the Interest Formula

If we return to interest calculation the reason for such exercises becomes obvious. Armed with our algebraic skills we return to the problem of financing the costs of the son's studies with the interest of invested capital.[45]

The problem was to determine the amount of capital "C" needed to yield a certain amount of interest. To start with we have only our interest formula, simplified for yearly interest.

$$I = \frac{C \cdot p}{100}$$

Here C is the number to find. It needs to be isolated on one side. If we apply our new rules, we multiply both sides by 100 and then divide by p.

$$\frac{I \cdot 100}{p} = C$$

$$I = \$30,000 \text{ and}$$
$$p = \quad 8$$

then we have

$$\frac{\$30,000 \cdot 100}{8} = C$$

If we then work it out we get:

$$\$375,000 = C \quad \text{or} \quad C = \$375,000$$

We obtained this result before. But at this point it is important to create confidence in the rules of conversions. The fact that our results agree shows that algebraic conversions can indeed solve problems.

Let us vary this exercise and use the interest formula once more:

Sample Exercise to Determine Capital C:
How much capital must the father invest at a rate of 8.5% in order to get the same yearly yield of $30,000?

If we place

$$I = \$30{,}000 \quad \text{and}$$
$$p = 8.5$$

into the interest formula for finding C, we obtain this:

$$\frac{\$30{,}000 \cdot 100}{8.5} = C$$

or $352,941.17 (capital C) is needed in order to yield interest of $30,000 per year.

As can be seen the ability to convert algebraic expressions proves to be extraordinarily helpful in solving the various problems connected to interest calculation. The interest formula can be used to solve interest I, capital C, interest rate p or time t.

Sample Exercise to Determine Interest Rate p:

Let us assume that the father has only $280,000 at his disposal. Yet he still expects to get $30,000 as interest to support his son. What must be the rate of interest to obtain this yield?

Solution: We convert our original interest formula so that p stands alone. To do this we multiply both sides by 100 and divide both sides by C. This yields:

$$\frac{I \cdot 100}{p} = C$$

$$I \cdot 100 = C \cdot p \quad \text{and} \quad \frac{I \cdot 100}{C} = p$$

Inserting our given values we obtain:

$$\frac{\$30{,}000 \cdot 100}{\$280{,}000} = p$$

The result, rounded off to two decimal places, is an interest rate of:

$$p = 10.71$$

Of course this must be a larger number than in our previous example because the same yield is to be obtained from less capital.

Sample Calculation to Calculate Days of Interest t:

The interest formula can also be used to calculate days of interest needed to achieve a given amount of interest. If we want to convert the interest formula to get t alone on one side, we need to go back to the formula for daily interest, multiply both sides by 100 and 360 and then divide by C times p.

$$t = \frac{I \cdot 100 \cdot 360}{C \cdot p}$$

Let us look at another example:

A machine worth $15,000 earns an interest of 6% per annum. How long does it have to work to yield interest of $3,000?

Solution: the last interest formula must be used here:

$$t = \frac{I \cdot 100 \cdot 360}{C \cdot p}$$

Our values are:

$$I = \$3,000$$
$$C = \$15,000$$
$$p = 6$$

Inserting these we obtain:

$$t = \frac{\$3,000 \cdot 100 \cdot 360}{\$15,000 \cdot 6}$$

or: $t = 1,200$ days $= 3.3$ years.

This covers all possible uses of the interest formula. Let us recapitulate the four interest formulas:

If interest I is to be calculated we use:

$$I = \frac{C \cdot p \cdot t}{100 \cdot 360}$$

If we look for capital C the formula is:

$$C = \frac{I \cdot 100 \cdot 360}{p \cdot t}$$

The formula for the necessary rate of interest in order to receive a given amount of interest in a given time is:

$$p = \frac{100 \cdot 360 \cdot I}{C \cdot t}$$

Finally we can calculate the time t in which a capital will yield a given amount of interest by using the following formula:

$$t = \frac{100 \cdot 360 \cdot I}{C \cdot p}$$

We can simply exchange the letters C, p, and t in the last three formulas to create the other formulas.

Practice Exercises
Group 7: Conversions of the Interest Formula
1. What is the maximum credit for the yearly interest (with no amortizing payments) of $5,000 ($10,000, $7,000)? Calculate this for an interest rate of 8%, 10%, and 12%. Enter the results in a table.

p/I	$5,000	$10,000	$7,000
8	C=	C=	C=
10	C=	C=	C=
12	C=	C=	C=

2. If somebody overdraws his account, i.e. he takes on a credit he cannot settle within the limit of his credit allowance, he has to pay 12% interest per annum. At the same time he collects 3% interest on his savings account for his deposit per year (the legally set period of notice). Between March 7 and June 28 somebody has overdrawn his account by $2,000. How long does he have to keep $2,000 in his savings account to receive the amount of interest he owes for the overdraft?

3. The following deposits and withdrawals have been made in the same savings account in the course of one year. Interest was always 3%. Calculate the final total as of December 31. (Interest is added to the account only at the end of the year.)

Date	Procedure	Amount	Balance	Interest Days	Interest
1/1	Start balance	$1,800	$1,800		
1/15	Deposit	$400			
3/22	Withdrawal	$300			
5/2	Withdrawal	$150			
7/17	Deposit	$800			
12/15	Withdrawal	$300			
12/31	Reckoning				

Supplements

1. The interest formula we work with applies to bank accounts in a bank only for times not beyond an interest term. Today's bank regulations add the interest to the capital quarterly, semi-annually or at the end of a year.
2. The interest formula has been agreed on by people because it appears just. Yet for long time periods it surely cannot be appropriate because the following could happen. A person pays a small amount into an account and leaves it to bear interest for many years. When he dies the account goes to his heirs. Now if one calculates the interest after a few hundred years, all the money in the world would not be enough to pay out this amount. But this cannot be and this has never been, because currencies lose their value and fortunes are destroyed. Could it be that the cause of this is an interest formula that is not quite correct? To demonstrate this we show the interest effect of 10% on $10,000. We add the interest each year to the capital and include it in the total capital for the year.

Number of years	Capital
0	$1,000.00
1	$1,100.00
2	$1,210.00
3	$1,331.00
4	$1,464.10
5	$1,610.51
6	$1,771.56
7	$1,948.72
8	$2,143.59
9	$2,357.95
10	$2,593.75
20	$6,727.50
30	$17,449.40
40	$45,259.26
50	$117,390.85
100	$13,780,612.34 $\approx$ 13 million
200	$189,905,276.40 $\approx$ 190 million
300	$2.6 \cdot 10^{15}$ $\approx$ 2.6 billion

If the $1,000 had been used to acquire a production tool (for example, a loom) and had the capital earned interest, this tool would have become obsolete due to wear and tear and the appearance of better looms. Thus in the long run it cannot earn interest. It ages. The aging process would work counter to the gained profit, even if the earned gain would have been used to acquire ever new means of production. It is simply a fact that the trees do not grow to the heavens. Would it then not be appropriate to institute an aging of money into the monetary system?[46] This could be done by using an interest formula in which the rate depends on the time r(t):

$$I = C \cdot \frac{p(t)}{100} \cdot \frac{t}{360}$$

This means that in the first year the rate will be maybe 15%, in the second year it will be only 14%, and so on. We could use a decreasing rate as every real capital-like machine does.

3. The basic rules for figuring interest according to the the method practiced in Germany are:

◊ Each month is figured as 30 days.
◊ The year is figured as 360 days.
◊ If the end or the beginning of the term falls on the 31st of a month the month is treated as having 30 days.
◊ If the end of a term falls on February 28th or 29th, February is treated as having 30 days.
◊ Determination of value is the date which determines the beginning or the end of the calculation of interest.
◊ According to the BGB (book of civil law) the first of the month is counted but not the last.

These rules are practiced also in Switzerland, the Scandinavian countries and the countries of the former USSR.

The French Method counts the days according to a year with 360 days. Besides in France it is used in Belgium, the Netherlands, Spain, Italy, Turkey, and Austria. In case of Lombard credits (certain credits of the Bundesbank to credit institutes), the German Bundesbank also uses this method.

The English Method calculates exactly to the calendar. Used in England, it is also valid in the United States, Portugal, Canada, Japan, and Greece. In Germany this method is applied, for example, in cases of legally interest bearing claims against private persons, e.g., in inheritance matters.[47]

4. Earlier we saw that money is a (legal) claim for other peoples' accomplishments. Therefore money does not have a practical value like a loaf of bread, a lamp, or some other useful object. This claim is printed on a paper which has little value in itself. But it is not necessary to picture it as a thing. When Mr. R received his credit he never saw the money in the form of banknotes. The amount was made available in a special account on the computer. If he paid a builder's bill or the invoice for a machine, the corresponding amount was transferred from his account to the account of the building firm or to the source of the machine, by computer. In the United States and other countries most money exists in a form other than notes or coins. Only about eleven percent—a very small part—of actual money is cash.

5. The exercise we used to introduce the interest formula can and should be the source of conversations with the class. We started off by introducing the interest formula from the point of view of the credit takers (Mr. R). Capital was treated as productive lending capital. In the case of the father's financing of his son's studies, the connection to the creation of value is still visible in the form of the printing firm. However here the reference to interest is in the foreground. One can certainly ask the class: Who really pays for the son's studies? It may seem at first that the father pays it because he forwards the interest due him to the son. But this money has been earned by the friend who owns the printing firm. But he can only raise this money if he includes it in the prices he charges his customers. Finally, the printing firm's customers pay a somewhat higher price than they would pay without the interest due the father. Thus the printing products are a little more expensive. For the consumer this has the same effect as, for instance, higher taxes. The father has $30,000 a year available from the total worth of the community because he has money. If a student receives a stipend from the state this is taken in a similar way, via taxes, from the community. What would be the best way to finance the studies and education of young people?

6. Many banks like to make information about money and the handling of money available to schools. It is good to accept this customer service. The banks know best the current legal situation because all money matters are strongly dependent on legal matters that are determined at one time and are subject to change. Yet some of these materials entail the danger that the banking side of consumption credit and interest yield are stressed. We have attempted to make our starting point the free flowing of capital (of the savers) and the positive productive output of the people.

7. Who will be able to care best for the money—the politicians, the bankers, or . . . ?

Percent Calculations

It has been proposed to work with percent calculation already in the fifth grade. If this has not taken place this can be dealt with along with the interest formula. In a curriculum leaning so strongly toward economic questions, a thorough treatment of this subject does not seem so very attractive. Yet in sixth grade a few days of instruction should focus on it directly. This is particularly advisable because the subject has some specific applications the knowledge of which is part of a general education. Some teachers may prefer to deal with this in more detail *ahead* of the interest formula. One can save some time working through different exercises if simple algebraic conversions are already mastered. Whatever approach the individual teacher wishes to take, we give a short synopsis of the most important types of exercises and applications.

Percent Calculation

Percent calculation is a form of *ratio calculation.* Here one compares the ratio of two quantities of the same kind (for example two lengths, two volumes, two weights, two times, and so forth) with the ratio of two numbers where one is 100. If w : g = p : 100—in words: If the quantity w relates to (same kind of) quantity w as the number p relates to the number 100, we call w the *percent value* and g the *basic value; g* corresponds to 100, *w* corresponds to *p; p* is the *percentage* formed in relation to 100. The equation then is:

$$\text{Percent value} \div \text{basic value} = \text{percentage} \div 100$$

Instead of p ÷ 100 one writes %, where the % sign is a symbol for *one hundredth.* The basic value then is considered the whole divided in hundred parts to which the percentage refers.

Examples:

1. If a medication contains 15 Vol. % alcohol, this means that of 100 parts of the medicine, 15 parts are alcohol. For instance, if one has 10 cm^3 of the medication then 1.5 cm^3 of it are alcohol because $^{15}/_{100}$ of 10 cm^3 is 1.5 cm^3:

$$^5/_{100} \cdot 10 \text{ cm}^3 = 1.5 \text{ cm}^3$$

2. A certain type of automobile drives at a speed of 140 km/h and uses 8 liters of gas for 100 km. If the same car drives at only 90 km/h, it uses only 6 liters per 100 km. What is the amount saved?

First of all, the savings is 2 liters per 100 kg. If we want to express this in percent, we form the ratio:

$$2 \text{ liters} \div 8 \text{ liter} = p : 100$$

If we solve for p, we get p = 25. The savings of fuel when driving slower amounts to 25% in this case.

3. If a road rises by h over a horizontally-measured distance, we say that the road has a gradient of h%. Of course the road does not need to go 100 m in order to have this gradient. It can rise for half the distance to half the height $^h/_2$ or for 25 m to rise a quarter of the height $^h/_4$. The important thing for the gradient is the *ratio* between rise and horizontally-measured distance.

4. A low energy light bulb needs only about $^1/_5$ the electrical power of an ordinary bulb. Expressed in hundredths this means that this light bulb uses only 20% of the electricity of an ordinary bulb.

According to the three values in question—percent value, percentile, and basic value—there are three types of problems to be solved in percent calculations: the percent value, the percentage, and basic value. We have stated the basic relationship:

Percent value ÷ basic value = percentage: 100

In letters: $w \div g = p \div 100$

If the percent value (w) is the question, we solve it thus:

$$\text{Percent value} = \frac{\text{percentage} \cdot \text{basic value}}{100}$$

In letters:
$$w = \frac{p \cdot g}{100}$$

If the percentage (p) is in question we solve it thus:

$$\text{Percentage} = \frac{\text{Percent value} \cdot 100}{\text{basic value}}$$

In letters:
$$p = \frac{w \cdot 100}{g}$$

If the basic value (g) is in question we solve it thus:

$$\text{basic value} = \frac{\text{Percent value} \cdot 100}{\text{percentage}}$$

In letters:
$$g = \frac{w \cdot 100}{p}$$

Example:
An insurance asks for 2% of the real value of the insured building as the insurance premium per year. What is the premium if the real value is $15,000?
Solution:
$$2\% \text{ of } \$150,000 \text{ is: } {}^2/_{100} \cdot \$150,000 = \$3000$$

Practice Exercises
Group 8: Calculate the Percent Value
Unless otherwise indicated, calculate to two decimal places.

1. a) 1% of $12.00   b) 2% of $12.00   c) 5% of $12.00
   d) 5% of $24.00   e) 5% of $240.00   f) 5% of $2,400.00
   g) 10% of $2,400.00 h) 15% of $2,400.00   i) 30% of $2,400.00
   j) 45% of $2,400.00

2. a) 1% of 30 lbs.   b) $\frac{1}{2}$% of 30 lbs.   c) $1\frac{1}{2}$% of 30 lbs.
   d) 3% of 30 lbs.   e) 30% of 30 lbs.   f) 1% of 60 lbs.
   g) $\frac{1}{2}$% of 60 lbs.   h) $1\frac{1}{2}$% of 60 lbs.   i) 3% of 60 lbs.
   j) 30% of 60 lbs.

3. Calculate to three decimal places.
   a) 2% of 1 liters   b) 2% of 2 liters   c) 2% of 4 liters
   d) 2% of 8 liters   e) 2% of 10 liters

4. a) 1% of $14,000   b) 2% of 14,000   c) 2.5% of $14,000
   d) 3% of $14,000   e) 1.5% of $20,000   f) 8.9% of $70,000
   g) 15.8% of $70,000

5. Enlarge:
   a) $20.00 by 5%   b) $35.00 by 10%   c) $46.00 by 25%
   d) $31.00 by 17%   e) $180.00 by 30%   f) $250.00 by 100%
   g) $250.00 by 200% h) $250.00 by 300%

6. Reduce:
   a) $100.00 by 10%   b) $110.00 by 10%   c) $120.00 by 10%
   d) $130.00 by 30%   e) $150.00 by 7%   f) $88.00 by 50%
   g) $1,000.00 by 7.5% h) $170.00 by 8.3%   i) $512.00 by 1%

7. A landlord increases all rents by 12%. What are the new rents for the tenants, if the old rents were:
   a) $720.00   b) $850.00   c) $600.00
   d) $1,200.00

8. If the value added tax of 15% is applied to most prices and sales, calculate the value added tax for the following gross prices:
   a) $10.00 $20.00 $30.00 $40.00 $50.00 $100.00
   b) $17.59 $28.30 $27.27 $54.90 $1,230.28

9. The volume of water increases by about 9% when it freezes. How much ice results from 7 liters of water?

10. A greengrocer counts on 20% waste of some types of fruit due to rot. He includes this in his calculation. He has ordered 60 lbs. What is the minimum he must sell to come out even with his calculation?

11. A tax of 4.5% must be paid when buying land. What is the tax on a lot worth $160,000?

12. A new school building is estimated at $12 million. A building firm makes a bid of 3% less then the $12 million. What sum does it expect to get?

13. 14% of the raw weight of coffee is lost when it is roasted. How much roasted coffee does one obtain from 40 lbs of raw coffee?

14. Milling grain yields 78% flour and 19% bran. The remainder is waste. How many kg flour and how much bran does the miller get from 1t. of grain? (one metric ton [t] = 1000 kg)

Practice Exercises
Group 9: Calculating the Percentage

1. How much of a percentage is:
   a) $18 of $36   b) $18 of $54   c) $18 of $72
   d) $18 of $144   e) 1.6 kg of 4.8 kg   f) 1.6 kg of 256 kg
   g) 9m of 18m   h) 9m of 27m   i) 9m of 144m
   j) 17g of 51g   k) 34g of 51g   l) 34g of 102g?

2. How much of a percentage is:
   a) $7.80 of $3,699   b) $34.70 of $10,000   c) $9.50 of $7,800?

3. By what % does a value increase if one:
   a) doubles it   b) trebles it   c) multiplies it by 10?

4. By what % does a number decrease if one
   a) halves it   b) divides it into 3 parts   c) quarters it
   d) divides it into   e) divides it into   f) into 100 parts?
       5 parts   10 parts

5. By how many % is:
    a) 2 larger than 1   b) 3 larger than 2   c) 4 larger than 3
    d) 5 larger than 4   e) 6 larger than 5?

6. By how many % is:
    a) 2 smaller than 3 b) 3 smaller than 4   c) 4 smaller than 5
    d) 5 smaller than 6 e) 6 smaller than 7   f) 99 smaller than 100?

7. 1kg of Baltic Sea water contains 18g of salt, 1kg of North Sea water 24g and 1kg of Dead Sea Water 240g. What is the salt content in each case in %?

8. 6 liters of milk contains 5.1 liters of water. What is the percent of water content in the milk?

9. What % of
    a) $500 is $75   b) $1,000 is $75   c) $2,000 is $75
    d) $1,500 is $165   e) $22,000 is $2,200   f) $1,350 is $780
    g) $34 is $8.75   h) $125.00 is $1.25?

Practice Exercises
Group 10: Calculating the Basic Value

1. An individual owns securities which yield a certain interest per year. But a 30% capital gains tax is deducted so that he receives only $1,750. How many dollars go to the Internal Revenue Service?
(Take care! $p = 70$!)

2. At the end of summer sale a shop reduces all prices by 30%. What was the original price of a dress which now sells for $35.20?

3. An individual looks for an investment. He wants his capital to bear about 8% yearly interest. He is being offered an apartment house which takes in $240,000 in yearly rents. What is the highest price he can pay in order to receive the desired interest of 8%? (Of course the yield is reduced by paying for repairs, property tax, and so forth, but we will not take these into account yet.)

4. An industrial firm depreciates the value of new machinery yearly by 20%. After 3 years the book value of the machines is $72,400. What was

the original value of the machines?
Practice Exercises
Group 11: Miscellaneous Exercises

1. During salary negotiations the question often arises whether all wages should be increased by a fixed amount by a fixed percentage. Fill out the following table.

Original wage	New wage with a $200 raise	Raise in %	New wage with a 5% raise	Raise in $
$900.00				
$1,200.00				
$2,000.00				
$4,000.00				
$6,000.00				

2. The price of one Euro has decreased from $1.02 to $0.98
   a) How much less (in percent) is the Euro worth now?
   b) What would be the price in dollars of a new German car that costs $30,000 prior to the change if the Euro-price of the car has not changed?

3. *Gross, Net, Tare:*
   The weight of a shipment is differentiated by: the gross weight (= the total weight of the shipment), the net weight (= the weight of the contents) and the tare weight (= the weight of the packaging). It is common practice to indicate the net and tare weights as a percentage of the gross weight. (Gross weight = net weight + tare weight)
   a) A case of fruit weighs 32.5kg, the tare is 8%. What is the net weight of the shipment?
   b) $160.80 is being paid as cash on delivery for a case of nuts weighing 27.5kg. The tare is 4%. What is the sale price of 1kg. hazelnuts if the profit is to be 25%?

4. *Abatement and Discount*
   Large scale customers often obtain an abatement from a supplier. This is a price reduction compared to the original price. It can be granted

for a variety of reasons, such as the goods are no longer quite fresh or are slightly damaged, in the case of a clearance sale, or simply by ordering larger quantities. Discount is granted as an abatement if the invoice is paid by the buyer within a defined time (often ten days). The object of discount is to insure that the buyer pays as soon as possible. Both abatement and discount are defined in percentages of the original price. The sale price, reduced by abatement or discount, is called the net price.

a) An invoice for $480 was abated 5%.
   What was the net price?
b) After deducting 7% abatement, an invoice
   was paid in cash with $837.50. What was
   the original amount of the invoice?

5. A commercial employee earns a gross salary of $2,870. The social security tax deduction amounts to 19.6%, the income tax to 22%. What is his net salary? (The income tax is based on the income bracket.)

6. A chemical solution consists of: substance A–7%, substance B–13%, substance C–40%, substance D–37%, and substance E–3%. More than enough of all substances is available, except for substance E. Only 150g of E is available.

a) What is the maximum number of grams of
   solution that can be produced?
b) How many grams of the other two substances
   (A and B) or (A and C) or (B and C) are
   needed or that quantity?

The Promissory Note

One can go back to Mr. R's furniture factory in order to to demonstrate a "Bill of Exchange" to the children. The new building is completed and equipped with new machines. The number of co-workers has risen to fifteen. The old joiners shop has been taken down and the site has been sold. This enables Mr. R to finance part of his new factory. At the moment he has little money at his disposal because some things turned out to be more expensive than planned and, among other things, because a few additional work stations were created. All this was applied to the new venture. Now he gets a new order for over $100,000. This promises good work and profit. It involves equipping a number of classrooms with new furniture. The items are to be made from solid beech. Payment is scheduled for 10 days after delivery. R promises delivery in three months.

R needs wood for the manufacture of the furniture. He works out the needed quantities of various thicknesses, sorted by table tops, side pieces, and so forth, and consults with a wood supplier. The latter is willing to deliver the goods in four weeks with the desired maximum moisture content (8 to 10%).[48] Payment for the wood is to occur 10 days after delivery. At the time the cost is $20,000.

R has the following problems: he only gets the money from the school after the furniture has been delivered, yet he needs it to pay the wood supplier. Should he negotiate a credit with the bank? The negotiating process is complicated and needs a series of checks, sureties, and so forth. This is where the *promissory note* comes in. Since the wood supplier is very familiar with this type of problem he offers to put up a promissory note to be signed by Mr. R. From R's point of view the promissory note is a *promise to pay* to be redeemed at a predetermined day, that is when he can count on the money from the school.

From the point of view of the wood supplier the promissory note is a credit from him to the buyer. This is called a *credit on account*, and a credit bears interest. This is how it is thought out: let us assume that R obtains the wood on March 15th and has until March 25th to pay. Two months later on May 15th the school is to receive the furniture and pay before May 25th. This is the promised day for payment. But the wood supplier has a right to receive his money already on March 25th. Were he to receive it, he could deposit it in an account and receive interest for two months. Since he only gets the money later he loses interest. He figures this out and adds the interest to the sales price. Mr. R has also considered this already and taken it into account when calculating the price he offered to the school for the furniture.

Under certain conditions the promissory note has an eventful life. Suddenly the wood supplier receives a favorable offer of wood from Poland which is to arrive at the lumber yard in his town in twenty days by train. The supplier of the offered wood wants cash on delivery. Since our supplier does not have enough money, he visits the bank with a promissory note signed by Mr. R in order to discount it. That is, he presents the note to the bank, who in turn examines it and pays him a certain amount. This is not the amount shown on the note because this will not be available until May 25th. Therefore a *credit deduction* is applied because the bank in fact gave credit based on the note and this must bear interest. This deduction is called *discount*. It is calculated with the interest formula. The costs of processing this are also added.

The interest rate (discount rate) of promissory notes is determined by the Federal Reserve Bank in Washington, D.C., to begin with. It applies to notes presented by banks to the Federal Reserve Bank or to its branches in the various states (the central state banks). The discount rate is revised by the Federal Reserve Bank from time to time. As a rule the bank increases it by 2 to 3%.

This means that the value of the promissory note increases from day to day. As payment day approaches its value comes ever closer to the value of the sum written on the note. The amount deducted when discounting thus gets smaller from day to day.

Usually promissory notes are made out for two to three months. Even if a note is made out for a longer period, it can only be presented to the bank for discounting three months prior to the expiration date (maturity date). Thus promissory notes are used to enable commercial undertakings to obtain credit needed for business transactions with a minimum of formalities. Strict laws provide assurances for the suppliers and the banks when discounting.

In the example of Mr. R he would not be able to carry out the order without a credit for the needed wood. The promissory note makes it possible to *create* a value. It is intimately tied to the process of creating values. Through it businesses are able to grant credits among themselves, and banks can grant credit to commercial undertakings. Of course this is possible only if mutual trust exists. This is why one of the gravest wrongdoings a business can commit is to default on a note. To default means that the amount written on the note does not get paid in to the appropriate account by the due date. Once this happens a business is in danger of losing its ability to use promissory notes, in the future. It will lose a relationship of trust with other businesses or banks.

Instead of cashing the note at a bank, the note may be used to pay another merchant or firm. In this case the previous owner endorses it, which means that he gives his name on the appropriate field on the reverse side. In this way the promissory note can pass through many hands until in the end (at the latest when it is due) it is presented to the bank or cashed by its owner.

The (promissory) note can also be used as payment. In contrast to money it has, however, a limited validity and, because it is a matter of credit, of loan money, its value changes according to the interest formula. It grows up to its face value in accordance to the applicable discount rate up to its maturity date.

There is one more remaining problem. On May 24th the wood supplier has a right to $20,000. If he accepts a note with a due date two months later he loses money, either if he cashes the note at a bank and the bank discounts it (that is deducts interest) or because he does not receive the interest he would have had he received the money instead of the note and deposited it in the bank to earn interest. The note is written for a higher amount to take care of this problem. When it is discounted on March 25th it should have a value of $20,000. If the supplier does not cash the note the value increases according to the discount rate. In this way his capital bears interest at the discount rate.

In our example, with a discount rate of 8% and 60 days to due date the note would be made out for $20,270.27, if it is to be worth $20,000.00 on March 25th.[49]

Different rules apply when calculating discount than those dealing with ordinary percent calculations. Yet we will not address them here. Textbooks on commercial mathematics can provide more information.[50]

Once one understands the nature of the promissory note, one begins to see what significance it has for the economy when the Federal Reserve Bank raises or lowers the discount rate. If the rate is high, commercial firms will refrain from using promissory notes as a form of credit. Industrial activity slows down. Prices have to be calculated on the low side. A low discount rate, on the other hand, facilitates commercial activity but leads to the threat of price increases, that is, to inflation. This makes it necessary that Mr. R calculate his prices very tightly because he must compete with other furniture manufacturers who may have enough of their own money (liquidity) to enable them to pay for the wood without promissory notes, in other words without credit and interest expenses. This enables them to keep their prices somewhat lower. The higher the discount rate, the closer must be R's calculations. The lower his price the less pressure from his competitors. R will increase his price a little.

The following scheme provides an overview of the movements of merchandise and the various payment and accounting procedures involving a promissory note. This involves Mr. R, the wood supplier, R's local bank, the Federal Reserve Bank and R's customer (the school).

The Flow of Goods and Money

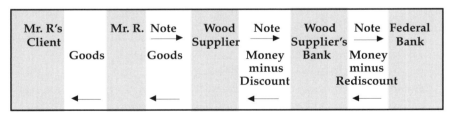

Accounting at Maturity

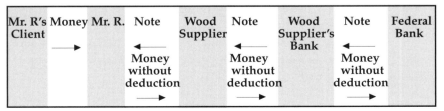

Example of Discounting a Promissory Note:
A promissory note for $3,500.00 is being discounted on April 4th with 12%. The due date is June 18th.
Solution: the number of interest days is 6 + 2 • 30 = 66.
According to the interest formula the discount is:

$$I = \frac{C \cdot p \cdot t}{100 \cdot 360} = \frac{\$3,500 \cdot 8 \cdot 66}{100 \cdot 360}$$

$$I = \$51.33$$

The cash value of the note then is

$$\$\,3,500 - \$51.33 = \$3,448.67$$

Practice Exercises
Group 12 : Discounting Promissory Notes
1. Calculate the cash value of the following notes with a discount of 8% on November 14th.

Amount	Maturity Date
a) $ 4,000.00	11/27
b) $ 2,500.00	12/13
c) $12,000.00	12/22
d) $ 6,866.97	1/15 of next year

Calculate the cash value of the notes.

2. Calculate the total value of the following notes that are being sold on May 20th to a central bank with a discount of 5%:

No.	Drawee	Place of Payment	Maturity Date	Interest Days	Interest Note
1	Levy	Concord	May 29th		$480.80
2	Helms	Lexington	June 7th		$1,060.00
3	Maguire	Salem	May 25th		$2,055.55
4	Warner	Boston	July 12th		$750.00

Appendix

Proposed Contents of Exercise Books

The proposed structure of this block is heavily based on observations regarding the economy. It leads to algebra (letter calculation) by way of interest calculation. In this way arithmetic is being increasingly emphasized. Mastery requires extensive practice. The purely algebraic conversions are primarily used to solve practical questions. I feel this to be totally appropriate for the sixth grade.

I have asked my students to record the short written comments on basic economic observations in their main lesson books. More tightly formulated explanations and rules were dictated. The class worked out the way to the interest formula so that all shared a simply formulated reasoning. A separate exercise book was used for arithmetic and sample exercises. During the working sessions questions about different forms of economies and the meaning of money were posed. The class tests covered questions about different forms of economies and the significance of money. Additionally accountings of work performed by time accounts and, of course, interest calculations were required. The instruction can follow a concretely thought out business transactions, such as supplying furniture to a school. Individual children can play the roles of the various business partners, including the bank, and write the necessary business letters. Finally, the entire business process can be described in a short essay.

This plants the seeds for an understanding of the life of the economy, to ripen in later years. If we follow Brater/Munz's suggestion[51] and deal with bookkeeping in more depth in seventh grade, it may be possible to go from a fictitious to a real business transaction where interest on capital is taken into consideration. (A book on mathematics for grades 7 and 8 is in progress.) Of course it is possible to have the children already in sixth grade prepare and carry out the accounting of a stay at a village school home and at least write down the calculations involved in a simple copy book.

Rule Booklet

In Waldorf schools the children themselves write their textbooks as "Main Lesson Books." In mathematics, too, this is routine. Yet when working with fractions in fourth grade, rules are being formulated for the first times. At times one needs to look these up again later on. In later school years other rules are worked out in a similar manner—such as the interest formula and the laws algebra. These too one should be able to look up. In addition to the exercise book students can create a *Rule Book*. This contains the most important laws of mathematics and their applications in condensed form. This can be a companion in school for many years and serve as a reference book, superior to the detailed main lesson books. It can help to add an index either at the beginning or the end and to provide it with a hard cover. Highlighting definitions and rules (sentences) in different colors can make this an excellent resource.

Practice Lessons

Weekly mathematics exercises should start no later than in the sixth grade. They make it possible to practice the contents of previous main lessons in a manner conducive to the creation of well-founded abilities. They also create occasions to consider one or two additional points of view, to add to items discussed previously, or to apply special cases of common laws.

It is not the job of these lessons to catch up or to become a continuation of the block. This would be just as unpedagogical as simply to keep practicing similar assignments.

A well-thought-out practice session demands just as careful preparation as do subjects taught in the weekly routine. A practice lesson may be introduced with some mental arithmetic. For example one could use calculations where shortcuts like $4 \cdot 25 = 100$, $8 \cdot 125 = 1000$ are repeatedly applied. In conjunction one could talk about specific difficulties in the last homework and the laws that surface therein. This can be followed by a discussion and review of the homework.

Without too much delay a new way of formulating questions is developed and finds its way into the homework. In addition to the assignments aimed at problem solving, where the formulation of a question is developed further, there should also be exercises leading to the formulation of questions from the previous lesson. These have been carefully discussed at the beginning of that lesson.

As I did in the formulation of assignments for written work, I have tried to offer a wide variety of homework so that every child could have a choice in keeping with his or her abilities. One needs to look at this in connection with the pedagogical task of offering an interior differentiation of capabilities in the classes. Children who have a hard time with independent problem solving should get a handle on the difficulties and laws that had been discussed during the actual practice part of the lesson.

A preview of the next practice lesson terminates the session.

Malfunctions in the Life of the Economy

Some time ago I visited a school in Eastern Europe connected to a tractor factory. During communist times the state farms worked with huge expanses of land. Large and heavy tractors were required. Since then much of the land was privatized and returned to its former owners or their heirs. Often the latter could not work the land for lack of small tractors. This presented an excellent opportunity for tractor manufacturers to build and sell smaller units. Indeed the engineers were quick to undertake the construction of such vehicles. In spite of this the factory I visited was almost idle. What was the problem? It was identical to the one Mr. R faced when he needed the wood to build the school furniture yet could not expect the money for his work until it had been completed. The tractor factory, too, needed many parts from other factories to build the tractors, such as tires, sheet metal, screws, and so forth. These suppliers wanted to deliver only on condition that they would receive the money instantly. Yet the tractor works would only have these funds after the tractors were built and sold. Because no tractors were being built the screw, tire, etc. companies had hardly any work. All production was at a standstill.

This is the ideal situation for working with promissory notes. Why was this not done or hardly done at all? Money lost its value every day. This resulted in prices increasing every day. The simple folk experienced this most strongly in the price of bread. After only a short time the price was increased again and again. This means that money is worth less and less. But when the future value of money is uncertain, promises to pay in the future are not easily accepted. One does not know what the money one receives will be worth in the end. Based on this uncertainty such high discounts and interest on credit are demanded that it is hardly possible to work with them. Therefore one starts to calculate all business transactions in Eastern Europe in dollars. In principle this is possible even if one does not have dollars. Therefore people who have not yet used capital, interest, and discount calculations find money management difficult at first. Trust is lacking and without trust modern money economy cannot function since all credit—even in the form of promissory notes—requires trust between business partners.

Further Topics on Economics

Which economic questions can be discussed by a teacher during his or her instruction to the children naturally depends strongly on his or her knowledge and interests. Many economic themes may also be found in Rudolf Steiner's *World Economy* as well as the social scientific lectures and essays—starting with the important presentations in *Spiritual Science and the Social Question* (Geisteswissenschaft und Soziale Frage).[52] These lectures contain many economic themes useful to class discussions. The reactions of the class will trigger more intensive and deeper involvement with these questions for many teachers. This can possibly lead to the study of the literature created by experts, based on Steiner's indications and dealing with the socio-scientific questions of the day.

As may be expected Steiner's discussions frequently refer to questions of interest during his lifetime. One can use them as examples to study how the basic thoughts and laws he developed and defined illuminate and explain present conditions. Only independent judgment, gained from observations of the present, can be used to transpose his indications to our time—if this is possible at all.

It is particularly important, and shattering at the same time, if one analyses the huge upheavals and changes of the twentieth century with the concepts and laws described by Steiner. Steiner's concept of the *social organism* takes its departure from dynamic processes. When these are in equilibrium they promote health and, in case of disturbances, sick situations. This would be the way of developing an *phenomenogical social pathology*. As a pathology of society this offers starting points for therapy. Some contributions to this theme are presented in the appendix. The 20th century is more than full of material on this subject.

The integration of social life into spiritual life, economic life, and life of rights can transpire as early as the sixth grade without a trace of rigid dogma. The example of Mr. R points to the significance of inventions in the economy. By making an invention R is productive within an area of spiritual life, aimed at the economy. By receiving credit he concludes agreements the essence of which are determined by general laws. A healthy state jurisprudence is the prerequisite to make such agreements possible. Yet the test for credit worthiness, applied by the bank and leading to the granting of credit, has a totally different character: The first concern here is to create a basis for trust in the capabilities and good will of an individual. This cannot be done according to common laws. It has to be performed individually from person to person. Thus it is a part of spiritual life. The fact that general rules instead of case-by-case agreement apply in many cases of current accounts (such as overdraft credit) merely indicates the fluidity of the boundaries between the different basic social processes and how they mesh with each other. By selling his goods R is primarily active in the economy. This is where he establishes the relationship between his efforts and that of his coworkers to the needs and capabilities of other human beings.

At every point of social life it can be demonstrated how all three basic social processes interface and interweave in different measure. This justifies the use of the expression *organism* because no organism knows of separate partial functions within itself but merely the interweaving of partial processes on and in each other. An organ or a partial function can be understood only based on the entirety of the organism and its relation to the surrounding world. In the same way the social organism can never be understood as *function next to function* but only in the relationship of each part to the whole.

Inflation and Deflation

A question can easily surface about the correct quantity of money within an economic community. In actual fact this is one of the most difficult economic problems. The purpose of the relative independence from all other state organs of the Federal Reserve Bank, as dictated by a basic law, is to prevent the quantity of money from becoming a plaything of political interests.

Using simple models one could discuss with the class what an increase or decrease in money supply would mean. If a model society is composed of three persons who produce different items and sell them among each other, then an increase or decrease of the mass of money would have no particular effect. If the amount of money were doubled, the prices would also double, were it halved, they would also be halved. The *relation* of the prices to each other is essential to the health of the small community. Each person has to receive the amount of money for his products that enables him to take adequate care of his needs. The *relationship* of prices, not the amount of money, is what matters.

But things are different if, as is the case in real society, values of money are tied to values of things. If, through inflation, money values lose buying power, the fortune shifts to the owners of things. In Goethe's *Faust* the fool understands this. He understands the inflationary effect of the paper money invented by Mephistopheles and announces, "This night I'll be a landlord, sitting pretty."[53] If high rates of inflation occur—as was the case in East Europe in the nineties—large numbers of people are robbed of their savings, whereas those able to get possession of land, houses or means of production can at times become rich very quickly. Huge shifts in ownership of fortunes occur. Slight inflation usually has a stimulating effect and is therefore not feared.

Granted that global economy with its international networks is hard to grasp, the important thing here is to establish an appropriate relation between the mass of money to the offerings of goods and services. Given a rapid flow of money, one needs altogether less money, and in case of a slower flow more. The national economies of today are tied closely together in a worldwide network and therefore the rate of exchange has considerable impact on the individual economies. Therefore institutions like the Federal Reserve Bank must carefully observe the national economy as well as the global international money network. The U. S. dollar long ago became a global currency which influences the value of many individual currencies. The price of energy (for example, crude oil) is one of the essential economic factors that determines the value of money. This price is internationally expressed in dollars. Should *deflation* occur, that is, a constant *increase* of the value of money, the effect is that as little as possible is bought, as everyone seeks money values, and the economy would die.

Business Capital, Loan Capital, Investment Capital

In dealing with economy Rudolf Steiner touches on the different parts played by business capital, loan capital and investment capital.[54] It is relatively easy to explain to the children that larger accumulations of money mostly occur from business transactions. A successful business transaction produces a surplus in excess of what an increase in business activity can absorb. The entrepreneur will then either invest the surplus business capital in his own place of production—if he wishes to be active in industrial production—or make it available to other people as loan capital for their activities. In the previously cited works Steiner discusses the political implications of the three types of capital. This can be studied more deeply.

Final Comment

If properly taken up and dealt with, using the appropriate background material, Rudolf Steiner's suggestions on the connection of elementary economics to mathematics will allow the teacher to face a transformed class. The children's vision goes out toward the social world around them. The life of their souls has taken root in important happenings of this world. History, geography, matter-of-fact statements in business letters and business essays and, finally, mathematics itself may assume totally new meaning in this block of learning. If geography becomes largely economic geography, as Steiner suggests, then a new light is shed on the foundation of cities at the estuary of rivers (e.g. New York, Boston, and Seattle), at fords of rivers, and other places that favor accessibility. These founding developments tie into the development of barter economies in such areas. The principal motive of the fifth cultural period, dominance of the economy, dawns in the activity of the Hanseatic union, and the establishment of factories, as well as the very modern economic structures created by the Order of Templars.

It would be a gross misunderstanding to be concerned that hands-on occupation with the economy leads to materialism. Rather, a healthy connection of the soul's life with material existence may well be the prerequisite for a good development of soul and spirit. Discussing the different sorts of money—consumption money, loan money, gift money—demonstrates that a healthy economy calls for a free life of the spirit as a natural companion. It is the very lack of understanding of economic processes that shackles us to their effectiveness.

It is surprising that, even in Western countries, leading economists have so little understanding of real economic interconnections. Often the focus is too narrowly directed at one's own enterprise and interests with no understanding of the unity of global economy. This is obvious in the fact that today many places teach management with minimal attention to global economy. When the Waldorf student finishes his classes he should have received motivations capable of being deepened and furthered in early adolescence by those who wish to specialize in this field.

Sociological Fundamentals
for the Class Teacher

The Three Basic Processes of Social Life

In his curriculum indications, Rudolf Steiner points to dual aims for the sixth class. The first is to deepen the child's connection to his human surroundings by understanding elementary economic processes. The other is to stimulate ways of thinking that lead to working with concepts and conceptual relationships through the transition to algebra ("letter calculation").[55] At this stage, the teacher deals with the dawning of the ability to judge which still needs time to ripen and mature. Much should be planted as seed in the sixth grade; one should not expect to find it as a practiced ability. This calls for patience in the teacher and for iterative efforts to stimulate elementary thought processes. If this occurs in rich measure in the sixth grade, the fruits can be harvested in later grades.

The content of Steiner's indications dealing with economics has frequently been overlooked or taken as unimportant. Without these observations the interest formula becomes a bloodless abstract idea. A large step forward in the children's developing consciousness is the question, "What has to happen among people to enable them to live peacefully with each other?" It parallels the evolution of consciousness in the third grade when agriculture and home building, along with the simple manual tasks of human beings in nature, are in the foreground. Insights into human social connections with mental powers are now gradually awakening and wish to be used. This capacity is needed to understand the nature of money. Of course a good part of the economic process can only be discussed with the children in fundamentals and illustrations. However, if the child feels that the teacher is trying to convey a deeper understanding of living with the burning questions of the time, he will learn more than the mathematical side of interest calculations and their applications. In addition to the extensive socio-scientific literature created by anthroposophical authors, we need to emphasize Steiner's *World Economy*[56] and—in spite of its dated style— *Toward Social Renewal.*[57]

The discussions in this appendix give a sense of themes which teachers might be able to make their own by studying an elementary economics or sociology course. In no way can this become an abbreviated text book, but merely suggestions of themes of interest.[58] Life of society, human life, as it relates to the interface between human beings, seems at first totally impenetrable. Does each individual not live a life of his own? Does not everyone pursue different aims and interests? Among the many needs, activities, inclinations, and so forth, is it even possible to discern fundamental structures? These and other questions must be the preoccupation of anyone trying to understand wealth and poverty, war and peace, spiritual creativity or cultural deserts and more, among groups of people. Steiner identified the basic processes and their conditions in real life in the socio-scientific field in a way that has not been sufficiently acknowledged to this day.

These processes almost always occur at the same time wherever human beings work together. They appear in the *relationships* that result whenever humans interact with each other. As such they cannot be experienced by the senses, they have to be observed in the *relationships* between events.

Let us begin by observing a few simple transactions of social life. Let us first assume that we buy bread at a market. We experience directly with our senses how the bread is taken from the shelf, the way to the check out, and the payment. The act of eating, for which we have bought the bread, will follow. We also know that many people were active around the bread up to the removal from the shelf. By going backward through many stations—the shop window, the transport, the packaging, the baking, the milling, the harvesting, we finally arrive at *nature,* whence humans extracted the grain and other raw materials. By way of our eating it the materials return to nature. In the process we can satisfy the need which made us buy the bread—our need for food.

Besides the processes leading to the satisfaction of our needs, much else has taken place. Often we are not immediately aware of this. For example, the act of removing the bread from the shelf created a relationship that would have made it somewhat difficult for another person to take it away from us. Then, when we paid for it, it became our *property.* This points to *relationships of rights.* Such relationships also accompanied the steps by which the bread came about as it developed. Even if not often mentioned or captured in writing, covenants were made all along the line to regulate such issues as the right of possession. Their existence would instantly become conscious in the event that someone tried to claim the bread we had bought for himself or even steal it. There are other social events where such issues of rights become more obvious. We shall deal with these in further examples.

There is a third social process involved with the procedure that helped us to obtain bread. Anyone who has ever tried to make bread himself knows how much experience, knowledge, and skill are involved. Various abilities of different people are constantly called upon, starting with proper soil preparation all the way to the final making and selling of the bread. As so often happens, one becomes conscious of what these abilities mean if, for instance, they are insufficiently developed in some country. We quickly find out that there is little we can offer to compensate for the lack. It is far from easy to acquire the needed abilities. Even if we try hard to learn one or the other skill, we can accomplish very little. Most human activities involved in social life need long and intensive preparation. Education and expressing one's abilities by one's individual initiatives, are the human being's *life of the spirit*. In the final analysis this is what creates a contrast between human culture and civilization and natural phenomena, such as activities of animals. No animal needs to work as an individual to improve its abilities, unless tamed and trained by human beings. Most of its actions stem from its built-in instincts, as these express themselves in its bodily motions.

The example of the bread shows how three totally different processes work together and provide the prerequisites for the creation and consumption of bread.

1. The actual production and handling leading to consumption
2. The entire flow of abilities that have been fed into these activities
3. The myriad of legal relationships between the different stages of the derivation of bread. All who play a role in these processes are involved in these relationships, which end up having an essential influence on the use of money.

Rudolf Steiner calls these three domains of social life: *economic life, the life of rights* and *spiritual life*. By using the expression "life" he defines the character of a flowing process as essential to the existence of economic, legal, and spiritual activities. Life exists only as a happening, as a process. It lacks a rigid, matter-bound existence in the same way that a line of surf at the seashore is not a thing in itself but an expression of forces as they play together in the counterflow of bodies of water.

Let us look at a second example, namely the purchase of a book. Here too we acquire a piece of merchandise with a history similar to that of the bread. There are no essential differences between a book and a loaf of bread from the point of view of manufacture and handling to the point of sale. The raw materials are taken from nature, machines are used for production, and buying and selling take place at the various stages of production. We acquire the book because we have a requirement. In these aspects then this matches the first example. The important *difference* shows up if we consider the relationship that exists between the nutrient value of bread to its substance and that of the content of the book to the paper. With bread the nutrient value is directly tied to the substance and is incorporated in the human metabolic process by taking it in. The material of the book, however, can be changed. We could access its content through other media, perhaps a computer screen, a magnetic tape, or by having it read, and so forth. Our relationship to the book is primarily not physical but *spiritual*. The senses involved and the media we use can be changed. These do not represent an essential condition to the satisfaction of our desire. The only time this would change in the case of the book would be if we were to collect books as book lovers, not for their content but for their appearance.

Insofar as the book and its derivations are merchandise, they fit into the economic and legal processes as does the bread (without addressing such things as copyrights, etc.) But insofar as the material production must be preceded by a spiritual one and as consumption does not have its focus on a bodily function, such as digestion, there are differences. Yet reading the book reaches back to the social life. Just as bread facilitates bodily work, the book shapes abilities, awakens interests, provides insights or stimulates soul and spiritual forces that flow back into our lives through our actions. The making of bread requires spiritual forces and abilities. In the same way we require food for our spiritual creations. Each one works in its own fashion interweaving with the other.

As a third example let us look at teaching at a school. Here too we can see the school instruction woven into a threefold fabric of relationships. Here the education of the children, the life of the spirit, is in the foreground. This is the goal and purpose of the school. Yet this does not place us in an area free of the rights sphere. In the United States school is obligatory up to a certain age, the parents conclude agreements with the school, the teacher has multiple legal relationships to his colleagues, the school authorities, and so forth. Rights too are constantly established and sometimes broken in dealing with the children—even if unconsciously.

A third strand in the fabric of the school surfaces when one looks at the economic processes connected with it. The development of the consciousness of this strand is the task of the inner administration of a school or, within a larger framework, that of the Board of Trustees.

Again we have the interplay of all three basic social processes. They weave together like three superimposed color transparencies. In a conscious act of the will one can place these three transparencies next to each other. In this way one can obtain three images of the school as a place where abilities are being formed and where human beings encounter each other, as a fabric of rights and as an economic process. No enterprise can succeed without having a clear objective. The school, too, has a clear objective, namely the education of abilities. In this respect the school is an institution of *the life of the spirit.*

Let us examine yet a fourth example. The representatives of different firms and societies got together in the Department of the Treasury in order to negotiate import duties, to be placed on natural and synthetic rubber, with the pertinent officials. The producers of natural rubber want low import duties in order to lower the price of their products. The producers of synthetic rubber want high import duties so that the production of synthetic rubber will be profitable and their product can compete with the natural one. At this time, however, synthetic rubber cannot replace natural rubber in all applications. Thus one is dependent on the import of some natural rubber. With high import duties many products become more expensive. From the point of view of the national economy it is important to create the highest values possible in one's own land. This is primarily achieved through industrial production. What is the government official's duty in such a situation? He can create an orderly procedure by insuring that every participant has a clear understanding of the situation of all other partners. In the long run a person may be considered a viable partner in the conversation if he is able to represent the position of his opponent as equally well as his own. All partners have the same right to present their points of view and to expect that they will be thoughtfully considered.

Regardless of whether the best solution for all times was found in this example (this was certainly not the case), it was still possible to create a compromise in this situation, that is, a mutual relationship wherein each one feels that his relation to the others and to the whole is under control. By means of a regulation rights can be established when a basic balance is reached between the participants. This enables each one to create a long term plan for the development of production, trade relationships, and more.

Here again is a procedure basically involved with rights and also connected to the life of the economy and that of the spirit. Numerous abilities are needed to lead such conversations. This sort of meeting also has cost implications. The economic effects of the regulation which was created are far reaching because they cause the creation and failure of entire manufacturing areas. But the central purpose of the meeting was the creation of regulated relationships among people who were now in a position to direct their actions within the agreed framework in a logical manner, all this within legislative rules, valid for all involved states. Should it no longer be possible to build such legal connections within an area, if such regulations are no longer abided by and if violations can no longer be persecuted, then society disintegrates in the affected area as though the sinews and ligaments of a body were cut and each limb could only execute senseless twitchings. The field of social pathology (the science of social diseases) reveals numerous contemporary examples that fit such drastic descriptions.

These examples have pointed to very different happenings in the life of society. These have common as well as uniquely different features. What they have in common is that it is always a matter of an interplay of all three basic social processes. They are differentiated by the *motive,* the *object of the activity,* which set them in motion in the first place.

Let us look at the common features. An understanding of social processes demands that one can differentiate between the procedures involved in three interconnected activities and how they play together. Steiner points to the human organism in order to exercise this understanding in a spatially more defined situation. Here three basic processes play together in a similar manner, namely the sensory-nervous processes, the activities of the rhythmic system (primarily breathing and the beat of the heart), and the actual metabolic processes, which are all together the basis of every movement. Any event in the organism can be understood only if the pertinent way that each of these processes is involved is perceived. Therefore it is necessary to think of the simultaneous action of three processes at the same place and—this is very important—to be able to observe the specific expression of these individual processes. The nervous-sensory system has the brain as its center, the rhythmic system its center in the heart, and the "brain" of the metabolic system is the liver. In an analogous manner the life of society does not take place in uniformity of all three basic processes, but spiritual, rights, and economic life create *institutions* from the living conditions of their specific activities. The existence of these institutions represents higher stages of development for society just as the differentiated organs of biological development compare to the primitive unicellular being.

Conditions of Vital Importance for the Basic Social Processes

Social pathology is still largely in its infancy. It is the future science of social ills. There will be a time when this science will be able to show much more accurately how deformations of social life appear in areas where its basic processes cannot develop according to their own prerequisites and where their joint effects are not ordered in the right manner. This does not meant that there could exist a static state of health of society, a form that, once introduced, would guarantee durable health. At any point in time the life of society is the interplay of processes that, taken by themselves alone, would lead to sickness. No static balance can be achieved, only dynamic equilibrium is possible.

The Life of the Spirit

As previously stated the life of the spirit deals essentially with the *formation of capabilities,* with *endowment* and with the bestowing of meaning, goals and motivation to work. The human being is ready to spring into action when he is able to sense tasks that are meaningful and that coincide with his aims in life. It is interesting to note that in countries where the human being is seen as the product of society, motivation to work is clearly diminished. Aims set from without and "motivation" by naming abstract ideas has, for the most part, negative results. This demonstrates how incorrect is the assumption that the human being is the product of society, in other words that the motives for his actions, the direction of his strivings and inclinations, can be understood as the mere result of outer influences. It is simply not true that the development of society is a continuation of what already exists. This is the great dilemma of all futurology. No essential impact of social changes, technical innovations or artistic creations is predictable because these are not necessarily the results of existing conditions.

Whoever knows creative activity is aware of the fact that it can happen only as the result of an individual coming to terms with a set of questions and that the answer to this questioning does not have the sort of cause and effect relationship to it, as would be the case between natural events. But we live in a society and hence our questions are triggered by this coexistence, by our perceptions and thoughts. In this way we add building blocks to our human community with our creative answers. In retrospect this affords a view of the total edifice of social development. This uncovers meaningful inner relations and opens the road to valid research, such as histories of philosophy, art, religion, and sociology. However, if the creative contributions of individuals are understood as logical consequences of preceding stages of development, a mechanical picture of development results. Such a picture fails to take into account the creative forces activated only individually.

One should not overwork such comparisons. This one is meant only to illustrate the relation of historically described development and individual creative accomplishments. The decisive, sensitive point in the spiritual process is the grasp of an idea in the case of an invention or a similar intuition in the case of artistic creation. This corresponds to photosynthesis in plants. The formation of new substance would be immediately halted were the green leaf to be isolated from its surroundings. The same would happen to spiritual productivity were one to intervene with determinations from the outside. A creative spiritual process can only happen in the light of self determination. Let the formulation of questions stem from what exists; it must be possible to search for the answers independent from all existing experience.

This even applies to fairly external accomplishments, such as the solution of technical problems by engineers. It was not in vain that the Soviet Union created free areas in Siberia where even the political atmosphere was more liberal. This was the only way for them to reach desired technical advances—mostly in the military field. In relation to other countries the rate of innovations in other areas remained terribly low, in spite of a disproportionately high numbers of engineers. Of course this was not due solely to individual inventiveness but also to the societal framework which cut off the introduction of innovations to the production lines. When light and air—individual ideas and the spiritual climate—are restricted, iteration of what already exists is the only output. In the spiritual realm only things already known are regrouped or modified in different variations. New solutions to problems are a rarity. Many personal accounts from Eastern institutes of research confirm this connection. Freedom is a prerequisite for all fertile life of the spirit.

The Life of Rights

Living conditions conductive to healthy legal proceedings are totally different. As previously stated, legal (rights) proceedings allow human beings to establish mutual relationships that open up areas of free action but that also set limits. All participants in agreements can affirm these only if each one feels his own position "taken care of" based on a mutual understanding of the situation. Provided that I am able to understand and respect the other's needs to exist, then I can accept the limits for my own actions as well.

Forcefully imposed legislation, aimed merely at domination, will always be obeyed only due to threatened punishment or sanctions. One cannot expect the weaker party to identify itself with laws that express domination. The underling will get around such laws wherever he can sense an advantage to himself and where policing is either absent or not enforced. This creates pathological legal conditions. Therefore, every healthy legal process must be based on equal rights for the partners. Only in this way will the life of rights express the recognition of the life potential and work potential of others or of shared intentions.

All the way up to the highest level of the state, the life of rights is in many ways the characteristic expression of the inner health of a community. Recognizing the equal rights of all genuine partners is the prerequisite of a healthy legal system. The human capacity demanded for this condition is the ability to perceive the living conditions of other people: thinking from the "you" point of view. Those who wish to nurture the life of rights must initiate processes whereby such perceptions are trained, such as the example involving the Department of the Treasury. One can shed light on further manifold aspects of the life of rights based on this basic condition. This also serves to show how all healthy life of rights is an outgrowth of an equivalent life of the spirit. Let the legal departments of the state police the observation of the law; its proper nurturing and requisite abilities can only stem from the life of the spirit.

Observation shows, once again, that sickness in the area of rights breaks out vehemently where rights are abused to assure domination by individuals or where large groups of people are not understood in their specific situations and are excluded from any serious influence.

The Life of the Economy

Nowadays the life of the economy is the dominant process in the consciousness of human society. Yet, ever since the appearance of modern industrial methods of production, this process appears to be torn into a series of polar opposites in an almost unreconcilable manner. Some such opposites are employer and employee, producers and consumers, economy and ecology, and others. It is obvious that these opposites are so tied to each other that they could not exist by themselves. Regardless of different political convictions in the present form of the economy, insufficient profits lead to a slowdown of re-investments and innovations and insufficient wages reduce demand. The economic process is basically unable to grow unless innovation and development of productivity go hand in hand with increasing purchasing power. In t at the same time any strong unbalance is bound to disrupt the whole process. Purchasing power and selling power relate to each other like breathing in and breathing out. If one of these two dominates for too long, the whole process suffers. This statement does not begin to concretely describe the structure of production and consumption. One can achieve the same turnover with a few luxury goods and poor general economics as with a good supply for all. The important point here is that the economy is full of many tensions between elements that, though often apparent opposites, are strongly interconnected, such as capital interests and social interests.

Yet human beings are involved in the economic process in very different ways. This results in opposing points of view. Social illnesses result when these differences are emphasized in a one-sided manner. If there are no ways to prevent erroneous solutions pushed by individuals or groups, such crises will intensify to extremes, such as Mafia-like organizations. Disregarding such extremes, justified interests based on specific points of view also lead to imbalance. Thus it is impossible to avoid deformity by finding a constant structure. Precarious exchanges of influence must constantly be balanced anew. This process is essential within every living organism.

Capital interest and the search for social justice have proven to be the most basic opposites within modern societies. One or the other of these interests has been in favor at different times in different ways right down to the political systems. The ideal of individual freedom and the claim for equal satisfactions of everyone's needs as the ideal of social justice were connected to this at the same time. Individualism, connected with "capitalism," has gained a clear advantage due to technical innovations, increases in productivity, and the resulting increase in material well being. At a more basic level socialism has been able to perfect a far-reaching minimal subsistence level in its area of application.

Adam Smith described egoism as the mainspring of capitalistic management.[59] Egoism is supposed to be the basis of all economic activity. The greatest possible wealth is supposed to be created if every person acts egoistically. However Smith assumes the existence of agencies that assure free competition, and so forth. Under socialism, egoism is supposed to be prevented by the state as a power with the wellbeing of the community in mind and responsible for the handling of capital, the development of new products, and their distribution.

If one studies the sicknesses which have developed in both systems, even superficial observation reveals the following. Where the capitalistic system fails to deal adequately with the social component, the impoverishment of larger groups and the disintegration of society are a threat. There are groups of human beings who, of necessity, are unable to bring their egoism to bear on the economy. Children, for example, are dependent on being provided for, carefully nurtured, and so forth, all without return performance. In the long run inadequate educational opportunities have destructive effects on society. The same applies to other failed developments of different weak social groups. Any economic theory based purely on egoism must include social components in a functional society. Failing this, processes of social disintegration get out of control and the whole structure becomes destabilized.

Such a theory has difficulties similar to those with the social surroundings when it comes to its relation to nature. Here, too, mere egoism threatens to release destructive developments.

Unfettered forces of capital have perhaps the most destructive effect where they escape all economic connection and are able to move, largely uncontrolled thanks to modern communication techniques. This is the case with many speculative businesses. Huge shifts in wealth can take place in a matter of minutes. Even if the resulting losses are spread over many losers and go unnoticed at first, they still impact everybody economically. The difference between this and robbery or pirating is usually not particularly obvious. For sure, in the future, ways will be found to fetter such economic banditry. But the motives for such regulations cannot primarily arise from egoism. Such motives assume a sense for community, for an interest in all of society. Even if this can be justified theoretically with arguments of egoism, the only way to solve the problems is to think from the situation of the other person. But this is an altruistic trait.

Capitalism cannot thrive without a sense for the wellbeing of the community. In the long run it has also been a failure in attempting to replace the creative forces of the individual within the economic process by state agencies dedicated to the common well being. After all, not the state agencies, but human beings have to make the decisions over the application of capital, etc. These individuals see only their own functions within these agencies. To the degree that social ideas were laid down from outside a network of relationships—the "nomenclatura"—was created. This practiced nepotism, supported by ideology, and recruited successors among incompetents. Restrained by Marxist–Leninist ideology, these people failed to recognize the source of innovation. In this way they did not grant the individual free space to be creative. The result had to be stagnation and paralysis, resulting in susceptibility to corruption, disorganization and so on. Wherever progress succeeded it was always connected with allowances of freedom for creative and responsible individuals—often in contradiction to the ideological concept.

The historical experiments of long duration demonstrate, more than anything else, how an economy as mere release of egoism or rigidly designed planned economy—apart from other consequences—succumbs to illnesses not intended by its originators, causing various economies to initiate efforts to bridge the antithesis between individualism and community. In part this was realized by the ideas of social market economy with social contracts of long duration. Here ways to balance the contrasts were discussed. If, for example, one compares the development of labor unions in England and in Germany after the war, one finds an interesting field for social studies. Different ways of social compensation were attempted in Japan. Here, as far as possible, consensus took place on more uniformly understood social events. The authors of the Massachusetts Institute of Technology study of automobile production in capitalistic countries describe a series of important details.[60]

It is part of the central task of the life of the economy to find a way of reconciling the need for goods with a free space for those who provide the initiatives for commercial production. The thoughts regarding economic community have yielded experiments in this direction. Yet failed developments, such as perhaps the case of the co-op, raise questions that cannot be answered by jurisdiction. Is it not true that there are threats of malformations in the life of the economy wherever management of capital, production process, distribution and consumption fail to be in concrete human relation to each other? Capital that disassociates itself from this central social task, market research that only determines needs in a static manner, consumption that is not related to the production process and its assumption, all these allow for the disintegration of the economic process to disintegrate because the individual elements are no longer consciously related to each other.

Rudolf Steiner's proposal for an associative economic order[61] tames the capital forces which tend to usury by tying capital to aims found by social consensus. Yet this order allows sufficient play for individual creativity and initiative when solving economic tasks. Functionaries who must represent general group interests on principle are unable to do justice to the totality of economic situations and needs. This can only be done by human beings who become active consultants, based on as large as possible an understanding of the different factors of the economic process: the development of needs, social demands, advances in production technology, organizational changes, and so forth. Beneficial tendencies cannot be based on a blind battle for power between interests but in brotherly conversation by comparing possible measures to be taken and their consequences in a professional manner. The spirit that lived in the idea of the Round Table, or earlier in concerted action, is the formation of economic life out of social consensus. This can never be final but found anew from case to case. One can start off by agreeing on the *procedure* but never on the results of such associative conversations.

By calling brotherliness as the prerequisite of a sound life of the economy, Steiner does not suggest a sentimental caretaker attitude but rather the necessity to develop the economy on principles based on associative conversation. Here the observations of preceding developments and the aims for the future are harmonized. One cannot describe the details of an associative economic order in solid forms. Its essential feature is the nurturing of manifold agreements wherein the aim of all commerce is to satisfy needs in the best possible manner so that quality, application of labor and capital, ecology, and so forth, are in tune with each other. Competition is appropriate in the battle of ideas. Solidarity and the wellbeing of the community must be in the forefront in the distribution of goods.

I point to the relationship of automobile manufacturers to their suppliers as a good start toward associative action. For example, in a competition-oriented economy a request for proposal for an automobile seat is published and the most advantageous bidder, with regard to price and performance, is given the contract. In contrast the Japanese automobile production is oriented toward long term cooperation. Should rejects occur with a supplier's product in the competitive economy, a series of complaints and sanctions is initiated. If the problem is not corrected the relationship is terminated. The calculations on both sides are kept strictly secret. The price question becomes a battlefield, and indeed is the basis for selection among suppliers. In modern production new developments are discussed with the suppliers at a very early stage of development, sometimes even an exchange of engineering personnel takes place. The calculations are made available to all and an agreement as to the real cost is created. Profits are shared by agreement so that even the price reduction after a "debugging" period is taken in consideration. It is only when quite new methods lead to higher productivity of a supplier and to cost reduction of products, does the possibility for additional profits arise. A few years ago this sounded like utopia in Europe and the United States; today it is recognized as a prerequisite for financial survival.

Developments after World War II show quite clearly that such associative practices do not impede the economic process but rather revitalize and strengthen it. This is not, however, to say that associative management must keep on increasing industrial production in every case. The associative conversation about capital needs, production methods, and working conditions would be the very thing to enable thoughtful interchange in dealing with natural resources and could lead to decisions not based solely on competitive advantage from a management point of view. Such conversations are the place where technical, ethical, social, and ecological points of view can be brought together and made to balance.

How the Three Social Processes Connect

Organic life unfolds in the interplay of different processes. In the same way social processes always interconnect, as shown in examples in the introduction. Yet these examples always referred to specific things or events. Here we want to take another brief look at the interplay of spiritual life, the rights life, and economic life.

Each one of these basic processes is dependent on supporting the functions of the other two. Every institution under the spiritual life will as a rule include a piece of economic life. Processes creating procedures involving rights and contractual connections also take place within such institutions. Institutions of the life of rights also contain a series of activities in support of the actual aims of the institutions.

Spiritual life works within the life of the economy in a similar way. An institution of the spiritual life cannot exist without an economic base. A commercial (life of the economy) endeavor cannot exist without constant resource to spiritual abilities and creative acts. These involve manual skills required in the production area, business and technical abilities, and the ability to organize work and capital.

The most basic way the spiritual life works in the economy is the educational process. All of us go through many steps of education before we can be active in the economic life. If, for instance, we look at the career of an industrial designer or development engineer, we can observe how the steps of his career relate to the three basic processes. Economically he spends the greatest amount of time as a consumer. He gradually enters legal relationships over a fairly long time. Training and becoming educated must start at birth, even if they do not take the form of traditional education. As a rule, training, acquiring education, and the development of abilities play the principal part. That which in our Western culture is understood as being generally educated does not as yet aim at the special areas that qualify one for a profession in the narrower sense. Every human individual should first qualify as *human* to serve the community before going through a narrowing in other areas.

Abilities that correspond to contemporary life of society are in the foreground during the phase of becoming qualified for a profession. Studies of this phase show that too narrow a training of skilled dexterity and manual routines, as during the time of apprenticeship, serve neither the young people's need for education nor the interests of businessmen who must take a longer view due to the changes in technology. They need much more than mere learning of motions or routines. What is looked for is flexibility, cooperativeness, willingness to take responsibility, and much more. Above all it will be important that, as he prepares for a profession, the young person gets to know his potential field of activity. His outlook will determine the world of work of future years. He must look into the future, based on ongoing research and a sense of the general development humanity. A connection to the tradition of a profession may be desirable, but the novice must apply as a driving force the changes about to take place in his chosen world of work in the next ten or fifteen years . As a rule this will not simply come from those who have created the existing conditions and are dedicated to them. Therefore all professional training and education must strive for fertile cooperation from the life of the spirit and from the institutions and representatives of the life of the economy.

The initial "get acquainted" phase at a specific place of work is the beginning of responsible cooperation with others. It often brings about painful renunciation. In case of a designer having started off with artistic impulses carried since childhood, this work implies another constraint. Artistic activity must take a backseat to technical and economic necessities, and many a designer feels like a butterfly with clipped wings. He may feel like a slave compared to a freely creating painter. Yet every industrialist in the consumer industry knows that in many areas success and failure of his undertaking largely depend on such people. The inept design of an automobile can endanger a whole firm. The element of freedom must not be extinguished, even when a designer makes the transition from the life of the spirit to that of the economy and has adjusted as a coworker. This element requires freedom as a necessary atmosphere. If snuffed out, routine, lack of imagination, and resignation will take over. Closer observation reveals that the economic process cannot really exist without constant nurturing.

In the future it will become increasingly obvious that economic prosperity is significantly affected by the social climate of any endeavor. In the long run such a climate cannot be fabricated by phrases or external measures to produce "corporate identity." It can be created only by having *everyone* participate in setting goals and creating a graduated structure of responsibilities. This means accepting coworkers as individuals and participants in the spiritual life rather than as mere production factors. Logically carrying out this thought in its totality will have consequences reaching into the ownership of capital.

A danger in the relationship of the spiritual life to the economic life arises when spiritually productive performance is planned and treated as merchandise. This may be appropriate in specific circumstances, but, as a general rule, this concept is bound to weaken efficiency of spiritual performance. One can observe this over and over in functionary-driven planned economies and in bureaucratically managed concerns as well. Mixing spiritual life with economic interests destroys urgently needed initiatives and in the end leads to economic decline. One has to expect that competent management will maintain the needed free area for creative activities, yet direct the formulation of questions and interests toward the economic process. This presents a fundamental educational task. The various domains of life must be presented so as not to be inimical, but rather as related to and dependent on each other. A gifted artist's renunciation, when he cannot freely create sculptures but instead gives form to everyday utensils, is compensated for by the fact that his creations are widely accepted in society.

The life of rights penetrates every economic endeavor in a manner similar to the life of the spirit. It connects to the economic life in labor agreements, in work regulations, in commercial law, in the legal form of the entire enterprise. Here too is a danger that the life of the economy will inappropriately usurp the life of rights. Such attempts at usurpation exist when the life of the economy tries to dominate social legislation, work safety regulations, ecological issues, and so forth. They may promise rapid advantages but in time they lead to pathological processes and damage far in excess of the short-term advantages they promise.

Hopefully, by this point the basic idea has been adequately clarified. Life of society is an organic process of the interplay of three basic processes, the economic process, the life of rights, and the life of the spirit. In order to unfold in a fruitful manner these three processes each have their own basic conditions. These appeared as the ideals of the French Revolution: *freedom* for the life of the spirit, *equality* for the life of rights, and *brotherhood* for the life of the economy. Once these three basic processes are surveyed with clarity, the way they interconnect must be studied. How is each one of them active in each one of the others? How does this allow the other one to continue its existence? This ideal basic figure of a *nine-membered* social form remains barren, unless a phenomenologically working social pathology (science of social ills) learns to diagnose and heal the potential imbalances. Such a pathology must be based on ongoing observation. This pathology is a decisive prerequisite for social health because social life can exist only in a state of unstable balance.

The Economy and Money

It is hardly possible to imagine the modern economic process without a corresponding monetary system. Where money has lost its function in part or totally, as happens in certain countries, the economy and the entire societal life that depends on it are profoundly disturbed. Today in order to properly grasp the life of society, it is essential to understand the monetary process and its connection with the economy.

Accordingly the Waldorf schools introduce the children in sixth grade to a simple knowledge of economics by means of interest calculations. This is done after they have been acquainted with value-producing human activities of the epochs of agriculture and that of house building in the third grade. Interest calculation is then the starting point for algebra.

In his *World Economy* lectures Steiner explains that values are created in two ways. The first form of creating values is when the human being transforms nature so that it can serve others. In simplest form this can start with harvesting and transporting fruits. But the derivation of a product can be traced back to nature in all material end-products. In this way it is possible to trace the sheet metal for an automobile back to deposits of ore in Kiruna in Sweden, plastics are often made from crude oil extracted from the North Sea or the Near East, and so on. Whatever product from man's hands contains a part of nature—the lights in a classroom, the walls, the tables, and so forth. If one surveys various things one finds different relations between natural parts and the contribution of human labor. Wooden panels used to cover walls, for example, contain less human labor than the parts assembled in a watch.

From a global economic point of view, it is very interesting to compare which countries supply others primarily with slightly transformed natural products (raw materials) and which are primarily engaged in transforming the materials with human labor. Japan and Switzerland are examples of countries with relatively few of their own raw materials but a high creativity of values. Saudi Arabia and many other countries of the Near East derive their wealth from treasures of the earth, primarily crude oil. This type of wealth can be dangerous insofar as it hardly challenges the development of abilities to create a manufacturing process, and the formative force of work has little effect.

The second way of creating values in the economic process takes place on a different level. Studies show that within Europe, in Rumania, and Portugal, a tremendous amount of physical work is being performed but these national economies fail to have outstanding wealth. This shows that the amount of physical work and the quantity of the materials alone are no yardstick for economic wealth. What really counts is *organization of the work*, single minded *application of capital* embodied in the form of production methods, and *rate of innovations*, the number of new ideas used in production, in production engineering and in the development of new methods and production aids.

Steiner describes the two forms of value-creation like two pairs of transparencies we look through. The first lets us look at nature through the medium of work, and value is created by transforming nature with work. The second one shows us work through the medium of purposeful spiritual activity in the form of capital investment. The peasant at his plow, the cabinet maker at his table saw, or people in a wood chip factory supervising the production process, all demonstrate primarily the first form of value-creation, namely transforming nature with work. In contrast to this, the second type of value-creation is perhaps most clearly demonstrated when a new factory is being planned. Here we observe the manifold and prolonged considerations, the decision making about capital investments, the positioning and the flow of production, and so forth. These example show clearly that one type cannot really exist without the other. Physical work without purposeful planning makes no sense and would therefore be of no economic value. And organizing activities would have no effect without application at some point in the material world. Yet the mutual dependence of the processes should not lead one to erroneously equate the two. There are some national economies where, by studying the symptoms, one can find what illnesses of society are created when one of the value-creating processes is underdeveloped or when their interconnection cannot be sufficiently ensured. In this case one finds chaotic execution of work, such as on-site delivery of the windows prior to the excavation of the foundations, or huge planning organizations which keep delivering plans totally impossible to carry out. The history of huge production empires like Ford, IBM, and others shows that even in Western firms deterioration sets in, at least for a time, when the intermeshing of the two value-creating processes is persistently disturbed. As in all other areas of social life, profitable success always takes place in a state of unstable balance which must be constantly maintained—just as a walking man is never *in* balance but must *actively maintain* it.

In order to get closer to the significance of money in the economy one needs to observe it in its differentiated functions. To start with it appears as a means of *exchange* or *purchase*, so to say as substitute for goods that in themselves cannot be divisioned off in the desired way or the transport of which would be too expensive. It is easy to talk a sixth grade through the sequence of steps of self-sufficient economy, barter economy, and money economy. There is no need of money in a self-sufficient economy where everyone takes care of only himself and his family. All contribute as they are able to social existence so that an exchange of work must follow by tradition. In a barter economy that which has less value for the individual is exchanged against what has more value for him. Thus both sides gain something. In essence it is always a case of two-sided connections where specific interests are equalized—merchandise for merchandise or service for service or service for merchandise. For tens of years it has been possible to observe what a hindrance barter is to the economy in a modern industrial country in East–West trade or in the multitude of attempts at exchange in the private sector in the socialist era. The basic principle of barter trade is that the needs for merchandise of the partners correspond to each other. If a person offers refrigerators against bread he will very soon have considerable difficulty in obtaining the needed bread. Durable and short-lived goods conflict, the question of subdividing is hard to solve, and transport is difficult.

If a merchandise is commonly accepted and available in sufficient quantity, the transition to money takes place. As previously mentioned, American cigarettes took on the function of currency in an Eastern European country in 1990. Everyone accepted cigarettes in exchange for other goods because everyone could be sure to find buyers for his cigarettes in case of need. Even the fact that the cigarettes became unpalatable did not detract, as long as no one succumbed to the temptation to smoke them. It is particularly interesting that the monetary function remained, even as the value of the goods declined. Belief or confidence remained that the value of the goods was present—and, in the end, somebody always smoked the cigarettes.

The introduction of money creates a *legal* claim to receive services from the social surroundings. This *legal character* of money appears clearly due to its validity (as a rule a state). States have recourse to laws that order the acceptance of their own currencies. These orders have teeth as long as the money is healthy. Therefore money is not a natural product, independent from a societal space and time constraint.

It is interesting to observe that, in case of disturbances in the monetary order, such as high inflation or false pricing of certain groups of goods, specific goods increasingly take over the money function or a transfer to foreign currencies takes place. Legal provisions in connection with money are rightfully considered to be important controls of the economic process.

The essential result of the use of money, as compared to barter, is that the mutual relation between those who perform the exchange is largely dissolved. When money is given for goods or services, a potential claim against the recipient of the goods or services is absolved. The goods or services in question can even be received by a third person. The possibilities of using double-entry bookkeeping to handle the resolution of reciprocal claims in favor of a group of people who work together was demonstrated when discussing the concrete form of teaching the sixth grade. I acquire a claim to the service of the persons who works with me in the area of the currencies validity when I receive a service or merchandise. The introduction of the vanishing point in a picture mirrors my individual position whence I look at the depicted objects, thus I no longer need to depict many partial views, like in ancient paintings. In an analogous way the money at my disposal allows me to satisfy my demands within my commercial community. In this way money acts as a national economic bookkeeping system representing reciprocal demands. Dishonest acts in this bookkeeping such as forgeries, or inappropriate hoarding or disposing of money, are directly noxious to the economic process and the economic community.

Bookkeeping mirrors quantitative aspects of an enterprise, yet generally does not represent the enterprise in itself. In the same way the money in a national economy is originally not part of the economic life, it merely mirrors economic events. This function is of inestimable value because, like a recording instrument, it indicates economic conditions in manifold ways. In the process of arriving at pricing, in particular, it is an indicator of productivity, availability of materials and much more. Even the phase of a phenomenological social pathology in its infancy shows recurring profound damage to the economic process caused by price manipulations in which the function of money is falsified. One can see this with formerly socialistic national economies and, for example, with the EU agricultural market as well. Excessively high or low prices indicate that economic corrective measures need to be taken. Manipulating the indicator may be compared to setting a clock ahead or back in the hopes to lose or gain time. Price derivation will be an essential task for economic associative conversations. As already referenced, in the automobile industry, such conversations between auto firms and suppliers are taking place with salutary economic results.

The purchasing event exchanges merchandise, that is work performed in the past, against user rights by means of the transfer of money. This money is always connected to something in the future, because as long as it is in my hand it is not yet merchandise. Thus a past and a future event are set in motion by the purchase event. Benediktus Hardorp often pointed to the fact that the actual economic process consists of two counter flowing streams.[62] Everywhere the stream of goods has the money stream as counter flow. Merchandise flows toward consumption, that is toward devaluation. Money creates future possible transactions. As consumers we are interested in merchandise, as active producers in money, not for its own sake but in order to continue to be creatively active. If we take money out of an enterprise and use it to consume, we lose the freedom to be creative. But, since the producer too must live, this is unavoidable. The only question is the degree to which this is done. If the total amount of available consumer money is too small, the producer will be unable to sell enough of his goods.

```
              money              money              money
Producer 1           Producer 2  ◄──────  Producer 3  ◄──────  Consumer
           product              product            product
                     ──────►             ──────►
```

Whereas goods have their inherent value, their monetary value is undefined. By means of purchase their value can be transformed into all sorts of forms. Money plays its specialized part due to this very intangible character. In this respect it may be compared to electricity. Electricity is not heat, nor warmth, nor motive power, but it can create all these phenomena. Georg Unger spoke about the borrowed phenomena,[63] that make electricity manifest, as an intangible phenomenon. From the generation of huge forces to the manipulation of data, electricity penetrates large areas of our technical surroundings without itself appearing as a quality. Similarly money, increasingly by way of the computer that in fact is connected to electrical processes, today penetrates the entire economic life without being merchandise in the true sense.

Where money does not merely stay within the flow of exchanges and serve the satisfaction of needs, a higher level of its use is created. It can collect so that it can start itself to build economic activities. For instance, when a trader buys merchandise, he needs trade capital to enable him to hold goods until he can trade them. If his trade is successful he will increase this trade capital. By transporting the goods he can ship them to where the demand is greater than at the place of origin. Given that the difference in demand is large enough, he then not only receives back his own trade capital but a surplus he can use to defray his own cost of living and possibly expand his business as well.

If the capital at his disposal grows to the point where the associated trade activity gets to be too expensive or immense, the tendency arises to include one's own production facilities. For instance to plant his own cotton instead of only trading in it, to invest in the transportation business, and so forth, the trade capital becomes investment capital. Pure loan capital may also be used in various ways.

Prevailing laws permit the use of capital in the form of money to be used as consumption money as well. Renouncing consumption creates the possibility to shape value-creating processes to a very considerable extent. The formation of capital then slows down the flow of consumption and can flow into the increase of economic turnover, thereby stimulating the entire economy.[64] For instance, when money is being used to build a factory, the efforts of other people erecting the facility are being paid for. Yet the value is not lost as in the consumption of a loaf of bread, rather it remains as invested capital. Bookkeeping notes the values created by these efforts in the books of the factory. The people who build the production facility can be paid in a timely manner because the capital not directly needed for consumption is available as loan money in expectation of future outputs of the facility. Financing the capital investment obviously calls for *confidence* in a future event. Those who give the capital do so because they trust the planning people (*credere* = believe, trust). But the future can only be anticipated by purposefully directed thinking. The granting of credit demands thoughts, abilities and confidence on the part of the participants. It is therefore a question of trusting other people. Therein a basic social gesture finds expression. It is ever so human and describes the most important fundamental convention in the economic area. This is the frequent manner by which an older generation creates economic possibilities for the next one.[65] Although this does not exclude giving credit to older people, yet on the whole this is the process, which, given healthy conditions, accompanies the constant renewal of the participants in the social life through birth and death, by growing into society and by gradually fading out. Setting aside ever differing individual situations, one can say that capital loaned on credit is taken up by new formative initiatives and thus becomes the expression of a *human spiritual activity as it lays hold of the material world.*

The trust expressed in granting credit can be further increased. Granting credit is like lending a tool for another to use for a time, but with the provision that it is returned. As a rule the giver of credit tests the aims of the endeavor and controls the appropriate use of resources made available. In a joint stock company this is done by a supervisory board. To a degree, the latitude given to the entrepreneur is more or less constrained by the source of the credit, the Principal Regulating Order. There are, however aspects of human life not controllable by constraining the use of capital. Both within the monetary process and within the entire life of society there exist developments pointing to a third way of dealing with money—after the use as purchasing and loan money. Every successful commercial activity leads to profits. Among other things these profits are necessary for the renewal of means of production and of a constant process of development. Moneys not needed for this purpose are primarily available as capital for new economic initiatives. They are held, as it were, for new ideas and abilities to render them fertile for the economic process. The market for certain consumer goods can be saturated—a limited number of people cannot eat unlimited amounts of meat. Similarly the available spiritual initiative and the existing potential of abilities may be exhausted. In this case the capital finds no application within the economic process. Excess capital mass is created and areas to invest it are sought but not easily found within the economic process. These days this is where the tendency arises to participate in the international game of financial roulette in a manner that may be compared to the transformation of the police into a society of insurgents and pirates within a state, to say the least.

The cause of the creation of these free funds points at the same time to the areas where they can have a salutary effect, namely wherever the *formation of abilities* takes place, that is, where the *possibility for capital formation* is being created. We have already explained this cannot take place in the sense of an immediate economic aim, because what needs to be released are the very initiative forces that fail to continue variations of what already exists and bring to life non-anticipated infusions to the life of society. This is a matter where trust in entrepreneur ideas and proven abilities is not sufficient. Here humanity needs trust in human beings not yet known and their spiritual potential, that is trust in the children and youth. Today many persons entrusted with great responsibilities know well enough that culture and education play a significant role in long term prosperity—including economic prosperity—of a country. In any measures by the World Bank the educational prerequisites of a country are considered, because without appropriate capabilities money can be used only at the lowest level, namely as purchasing- or consumption money.

The prerequisites for the development of creativity and willingness to take responsibility are not adequately understood in our time. Overall, education is still looked upon by far too many people as a commercial enterprise. This either produces "human capital" to order as a planned product of a technical production line, or the task of schooling is understood as generating loyalty to existing power structures. The atmosphere necessary for a fertile spiritual life is freedom in the formative encounters between generations and spiritual pursuits in all areas of culture. This freedom is still being most violently resisted or, at least understood, only as a right to be bought for huge sums of money.

Beyond consumption and loan money there must be money intended to serve the entire life of society in a salutary manner. This money must be made available by individual acts of will and put at the disposal of the tasks of spiritual life. These must no longer be directly associated with commercial aspirations.

In fact most countries withdraw some money from directly commercial aims for a different purpose. This is primarily done through taxes and donations. In both cases this involves renunciation. The money is earmarked to develop specific areas of life in such a way that they are not directly subject to commercial interests. The magnitude of these funds, compared to the net social product of a country and their use for non-commercial purposes, is a very essential indicator of the inner condition of a society. Yet, in spite of this there remains a largely unresolved problem, namely that of administering such funds to safeguard them from encroachment on the part of the political-rights life or commercial life. Independence of persons creatively active in the life of the spirit is only to often still regarded as a danger that could interfere with other aims.

This represents a multitude of problems awaiting future solution. Their solution will create a decisive starting point for the legal configuration of the monetary process. The transition to this third form of money, that is, releasing it to the life of the spirit, is in many ways not taking place yet in a healthy manner. This problem is a cancerous growth within the global society, as it pervades the game of international speculations.

A teacher may harbor thoughts like these as he gradually tackles the task of explaining social life to the children. Of course it makes no sense to present dogmatic ideas of how society should be. In mathematics one gathers the stones of a mosaic to create an understanding of numbers and the world of space. These come together to create a larger image of the world of mathematics. In this way one can work on specific phenomena within society with the children and gradually show the laws that connect these. In accordance with Steiner's suggestion, it is necessary to start with observations regarding money as it relates to mathematics and particularly to algebra and in connection with the economy. The latter is also being developed in the framework of geography and history. In geography we are more concerned with the basis in nature, the physical configuration of the earth, the places where mineral resources are to be found, climatic conditions, transportation systems, and so forth. In history we deal with the development of consciousness in the human race in relation to commercial transactions and their embodiments. Starting with the commercial impulses emanating from the Crusades, on to the effects of the Hanseatic towns and the consequences of the voyages of discovery all the way to industrialization and capitalization of the economy, we see a sweep of events. This should keep resonating in all other historical themes during the time of class learning.

It is a vast assignment to prepare the child to understand society so as to provide the tableau of living developmental processes which increasingly demand his responsible collaboration. This task demands that the teacher himself be a contemporary participant in the life of society. When he talks about society he earns the children's trust only by personally carrying responsibilities within the framework of his own life and working together with others with responsibilities. Life in our society is no theory to be transmitted by thoughts, but life in which we all participate.

Answers to Practice Exercises

Group 1, pgs. *59–60* (Note: solutions to exercises sets #2 and #4 are already provided.)

1.

C	p	Interest time	d	I
$300.00	10	3/21 to 5/21	60	$5.00
$500.00	12	3/21 to 5/28	67	$11.17
$7,000.00	12	3/21 to 6/4	73	$170.33
$3,600.00	12	4/1 to 12/9	248	$297.60
$4,800.00	14	4/21 to 8/7	106	$197.87
$7,200.00	14	4/21 to 8/7	106	$296.80
$12,723.18	14.5	3/6 to 12/12	276	$1,414.37

3.

Machine price	Interest rate %	Purchase date	Date 1st payment	Amount 1st payment	$ still owed	Date due	I_1	I_2	Amount remaining payment
$20,000	10	3/3	5/3	10,000	10,000	8/3	333.33	250.00	$10,583.33
$36,000	12	3/3	6/3	12,000	24,000	10/3	1,080.00	960.00	$26,040.00
$120,000	12	3/3	6/5	50,000	70,000	10/12	3,680.00	4,316.67	$77,996.67
$24,000	11	5/2	5/28	18,000	6,000	30/9	190.67	223.67	$6,414.34

5.

1. Rate: $20,000 + $10,800 = $30,800
2. Rate: $20,000 + $9,000 = $29,000
3. Rate: $20,000 + $7,200 = $27,200
4. Rate: $20,000 + $5,400 = $25,400
5. Rate: $20,000 + $3,600 = $23,600
6. Rate: $20,000 + $1,800 = $21,800

Group 2, *p. 65*

1) $C = 35$ 2) $C = 300$ 3) $C = 30$

4) $C = 10$ 5) $r = 3$ 6) $S = 1$

7) $x = 5$ 8) $x = 6$ 9) $d = 10$

10) $r = 6$ 11) $y = 100$ 12) $r = 3$

13) $u = \frac{5}{2} = 2.5$ 14) $v = \frac{11}{4} = 2.75$ 15) $v = 2$

16) $v = \frac{13}{7} \approx 1.86$ 17) $w = \frac{2}{11} \approx 0.18$ 18) $w = \frac{5}{33} \approx 0.15$

19) $w = \frac{1}{3}$ 20) $a = 5$

Group 3, *p. 66*

1) $u = \frac{7}{v} = \frac{7}{u}$ 2) $u \cdot v = 7, \quad u = \frac{7}{v}$ 3) $x = \frac{13}{y}, \quad y = \frac{13}{x}$

4) $x \cdot y = 13, \quad x = \frac{13}{y}$ 5) $2u = 7v, \quad v = \frac{2}{7}u$ 6) $\frac{20}{t} = 2x, \quad t = \frac{10}{x}$

7) $\frac{20}{d} = 2x, \quad x = \frac{10}{d}$ 8) $81r = 192t, \quad r = \frac{64}{27}t$ 9) $17ab = 119b, \quad a = 7$

Group 4, *p. 69*

1) $18 = \frac{6a}{5}, \quad a = 15$ 2) $21 = \frac{3b}{5}, \quad b = 35$ 3) $28 = \frac{2c}{3}, \quad c = 42$

4) $29 = \frac{2d}{3}, \quad d = 43.5$ 5) $27 = \frac{3e}{2}, \quad e = 18$ 6) $28 = \frac{3f}{2}, \quad f = 18.66$

7) $2 = \frac{7g}{4}, \quad g = 8$ 8) $3 = \frac{3h}{5}, \quad h = 5$ 9) $2 = \frac{4i}{3}, \quad i = 3$

10) $1 = \frac{2j}{3}, \quad j = 3$ 11) $\frac{3}{2} = \frac{2}{3}k, \quad k = 9$ 12) $\frac{2}{3} = \frac{2}{3}L, \quad L = 1$

Group 5, *pgs. 69–70*

1) $v = \frac{u}{3}$ 2) $r = \frac{t}{2}$ 3) $y = 2x$

4) $u = 5v, \quad v = \frac{u}{5}$ 5) $x = \frac{y}{2}$ 6) $w = \frac{r \cdot x}{3}, \quad r = \frac{3w}{x}$

7) $w = \frac{2r \cdot x}{3u}, \quad r = \frac{3w \cdot u}{2x} \quad u = \frac{2r \cdot x}{3w}$

8) $a = \frac{c \cdot d}{b}, \quad b = \frac{c \cdot d}{a}, \quad c = \frac{a \cdot b}{d}, \quad d = \frac{a \cdot b}{c}$

9) $a = \frac{x \cdot y \cdot z}{b \cdot c}, \quad b = \frac{x \cdot y \cdot z}{a \cdot c}, \quad c = \frac{x \cdot y \cdot z}{a \cdot b}, \quad x = \frac{a \cdot b \cdot c}{y \cdot z}, \quad y = \frac{a \cdot b \cdot c}{x \cdot z}, \quad z = \frac{a \cdot b \cdot c}{x \cdot y}$

Group 6, *p. 70*

1) a = 3   12 = 4 • 3,   b = 3, 36 = 12 • 3,   c = 4, 72 = 18 • 4
   d = 25   50 = 2 • 25,   e = 4, 720 = 180 • 4,   f = 4, 7200 = 4 • 1800
   g = 9   171 = 19 • 9,   h = 139, 2,363 = 17 • 139

2) a = $^1/_2$, 2 = 4 • $^1/_2$ b = $^1/_2$, 3 = 6 • $^1/_2$ c = $^1/_2$, 4 = 8 • $^1/_2$

   d = $^1/_3$, 3 = 9 • $^1/_3$ e = $^2/_3$, 6 = 9 • $^2/_3$ f = $^3/_2$, 12 = 8 • $^3/_2$
   g = $^4/_3$, 16 = 12 • $^4/_3$ h = $^8/_7$, 32 = 28 • $^8/_7$

3) a = $^7/_2$, 7 = 2 • $^7/_2$ b = $^{13}/_7$, 13 = 7 • $^{13}/_7$ c = 3, 51 = 17 • 3

   d = $^4/_3$, 64 = 48 • $^4/_3$ e = $^5/_4$, 120 = 96 • $^5/_4$ f = 2, 1024 = 512 • 2

   g = 16, 896 = 56 • 16   h = $^1/_7$, 1 = 7 • $^1/_7$

4) a = $^1/_{14}$, $^1/_7$ = 2 • $^1/_{14}$ b = $^1/_7$, $^2/_7$ = 2 • 1   c = $^3/_{14}$, $^3/_7$ = 2 • $^3/_{14}$

   d = $^2/_7$, $^4/_7$ = 2 • $^2/_7$ e = $^2/_7$, $^6/_7$ = 3 • $^2/_7$ f = $^3/_7$, $^9/_7$ = 3 • $^3/_7$

   g = $^4/_7$, $^{12}/_7$ = 3 • $^4/_7$ h = $^{13}/_{15}$, $^{13}/_5$ = 3 • $^{13}/_{15}$

5) a = 2, 1 = $^1/_2$ • 2   b = 4, 2 = $^1/_2$ • 4   c = 6, 3 = $^1/_2$ • 6

   d = 9, 1 = $^1/_2$ • 2   e = 12, 3 = $^1/_4$ • 12   f = 30, 5 = $^1/_6$ • 30

   g = 136, 17 = $^1/_8$ • 136   h = 46, 2 = $^1/_{23}$ • 46

6) a = 0.2, 3 • 0.2 = 0.6   b = 0.7, 4 • 0.7 = 2.8   c = 0.7, 5 • 0.7 = 3.5
   d = 0.71, 5 • 0.71 = 3.55   e = 7.1, 5 • 7.1 = 35.5
   f = 0.07, 7 • 0.07 = 0.49   g = 0.7, 7 • 0.7 = 4.9   h = 7, 7 • 7 = 49

7) a = $3.65   b = $6.04 c = $4.01
   d = $2.15   e = $23.40 f = $250.60
   g = $1,308.30   h = $7.00

Group 7, *pgs. 74–75*

1.

p/z	$5,000	$10,000	$7,000
8	C= $62,500	C= $125,000	C= $87,500
10	C= $50,000	C= $100,000	C= $70,000
12	C= $41,667	C= $83,333	C= $58,333

2. $t = 111$ debit interest $= \dfrac{\$2,000 \cdot 12 \cdot 111}{100 \cdot 360} = \$74.00$

$t = \dfrac{100 \cdot 360I}{C \cdot p} = \dfrac{36,000 \cdot 74}{2,000 \cdot 3} = 444$ days

3.

Date	Procedure	Amount	Balance	Interest Days	Interest
1/1	Start balance	$1,800.00	$1,800.00	14	$2.20
1/15	Deposit	$400.00	$2,200.00	67	$12.28
3/22	Withdrawal	$300.00	$1,900.00	40	$6.33
5/2	Withdrawal	$150.00	$1,750.00	75	$10.94
7/17	Deposit	$800.00	$2,550.00	148	$31.45
12/15	Withdrawal	$300.00	$2,250.00	15	$2.81
12/31	Reckoning		$2,315.91		$65.91

Group 8, *pgs. 81–83*

1. a) 12¢ b) 24¢ c) 60¢ d) $1.20
    e) $12.00 f) $120.00 g) $240.00 h) $360.00
    i) $720.00 j) $1,080.00

2. a) 0.30 lbs. b) 0.15 lbs. c) .45 lbs.
    d) 2.7 lbs e) 9 lbs. f) .6 lbs.
    g) .3 lbs. h) .9 lbs i) 1.8 lbs.
    j) 18 lbs.

3. a) 0.02 L b) 0.04 L c) 0.08 L d) 0.16 L
    e) 0.20 L

4. a) $140.00   b) $280.00   c) $350.00   d) $420.00
    e) $300.00   f) $6,230.00   g) $11,060.00

5. a) $21.00   b) $38.50   c) $57.50   d) $36.27
    e) $234.00   f) $500.00   g) $750.00   h) $1,000.00

6. a) $90.00   b) $99.00   c) $108.00   d) $91.00
    e) $139.50   f) $44.00   g) $925.00   h) $155.89
    i) $506.88

7. a) $806.40   b) $952.00   c) $672.00   d) $1,344.00

8. a) $1.50; $3.00; $4.50; $6.00; $7.50; $15.00
    b)$2.63; $4.35; $4.09; $8.24; $184.54

9. 7.63 L   10. 48 kg   11. $7,200.00

12. $11,640,000.00   13. 34.4 kg   14. 780 kg flour and 180 kg bran

Group 9, *pgs. 83–84*

1. a) 50   b) 33.33   c) 25   d) 12.5
    e) 33.33   f) 0.625   g) 50   h) 33.33
    i) 6.25   j) 33.33   k) 66.67   l) 33.33

2. a) 2.11   b) 0.35   c) 0.12

3. a) 100   b) 300   c) 1,000

4. a) 50   b) 66.67   c) 75   d) 80
    e) 90   f) 99

5. a) 100   b) 50   c) 33.33   d) 25
    e) 20

6. a) 33.33   b) 25   c) 20   d) 16.67
    e) 14.29   f) 1

7. 1.8%   2.4%   24%

8. 85%

9. a) 15   b) 7.5   c) 3.75   d) 11
    e) 10   f) 57.78   g) 25.74   h) 1

Group 10, *p. 84*

1. $750.00

2. $50.29 rounded off to $50.30

3. $3,000,000

4. $72,400.00 after 3 years at 40%

$$g = \frac{w \cdot 100}{p} = \frac{72,400 \cdot 100}{40} = \$181,000.00$$

Group 11, pgs. *85–86*

1.

Original wage	New wage with a $200 raise	Raise in %	New wage with a 5% rasise	Raise in $
$900.00	$1,100.00	22.22%	$945.00	$45.00
$1,200.00	$1,400.00	16.67%	$1,260.00	$60.00
$2,000.00	$2,200.00	10.00%	$2,100.00	$100.00
$4,000.00	$4,200.00	5.00%	$4,200.00	$200.00
$6,000.00	$6,200.00	3.33%	$6,300.00	$300.00

2.   a) 3.9%   b) $28,830

3.   a) 29.90 kg
       b) The net weight is 26.40 kg. The cost per kg is $6.09. In order to have a profit of 25% the price must be $7.61 per kg.

4.   a) $456.00   b) $900.54

5. $1,676.08

6.   a) 5,000 g = 5 kg b) A 350 g, B650 g, C 2,000 g, D 1,1850g

Group 12, *p. 91*

1.

Amount borrowed	Maturity date	Interest days	Discount	Cash value
a) $4,000.00	11/27	13	$11.56	$3,988,44
b) $2,500.00	12/13	29	$16.11	$2,483.89
c) $12,000.00	12/22	38	$101.33	$11,898.67
d) $6,866.97	1/15	61	$93.09	$6,773.88

2.

Amount borrowed	Maturity date	Interest days	Discount	Cash value
$480.80	5/29	9	60¢	$480.20
$1,060.00	6/7	17	$2.50	$1,057.50
$2,055.55	5/25	5	$1.43	$2,054.12
$750.00	7/12	52	$5.42	$744.58

The entire amount is $4,366.40.

Overview of the Mathematics Curriculum for Grades 1 to 8

Introduction

The following information deals with proposals for distribution of mathematical subjects in each class of lower and middle Waldorf schools.[66] These proposals do not replace Rudolf Steiner's suggestions as published by E.A.K. Stockmeyer. In fact accurate knowledge of the latter is being assumed. These suggestions are in part very condensed and require further details. They have been discussed among mathematics teachers and have been largely notated. The suggestions for subject sequences in particular have been thoroughly discussed with Georg Glöcker, head of the mathematical/astronomical section at the Goetheanum in Dornach, Switzerland.

Of course each teacher should configure mathematical instruction freely in a responsible manner. But free methodical configuration is dependent, perhaps in the teaching of mathematics more than in any other field, on secure knowledge of the subject. Louis Locher-Ernst's book *Arithmetic and Algebra* can help the teacher to this competent knowledge. Once he is sure of himself, he will be able to deal with much that he may at first consideration too difficult for the children, if attempted at their indicated age.

One needs to bear in mind that the book was not written for schools primarily, but for students in a Swiss technical school. Then teachers will read selections for the most important subjects and keep in mind that many of the problems are too difficult for the school. Some specific chapters and, as the case may be, specific pages are referred to, in order to ease this situation. At least we as teachers should cover the material in the chapters indicated.

The methodological-didactic fundamentals for teaching mathematics are not found in *Arithmetic and Algebra*. Many suggestions on this subject may be found in Rudolf Steiner's lectures and the writings and essays of Herman von Baravalle, Arnold Bernhard, Ernst Bindel, Ernst Schuberth, Ron Jarman, Bengt Ulin, and others. References to projective geometry only stress aspects dealt with in later mathematical instruction. Other publications on the teaching of mathematics are referred to on a case-to-case basis.

A selection of related literature on the teaching of mathematics in Waldorf schools, beyond the framework of the first eight years, may be found in this author's book *Beginning Instruction of Mathematics in Waldorf Schools* [Der Anfangsunterricht in der Mathematik an Waldorfschulen]. (See Footnote 1.)

Those who wish to go more deeply into Steiner's suggestions on this subject, as well as gain an anthroposophical understanding of mathematics, will be grateful for the collection of material *Rudolf Steiner on Mathematics* [Rudolf Steiner zur Mathematik], collected by U. Kilthau and G. Schrader (to be published by AWSNA Publications).

Grade One
The first numerical concepts are introduced by starting with the unit, which corresponds in some respects to that of "set." (See Steiner's course *The Art of Education based on a Grasp of the Essence of the Human Being*, GA 311, fifth lecture and questions and answers). Steiner first introduces Roman numerals in connection to a discussion of unity, duality, and trinity. The Arabic numbers need to be treated early on as well. Calculations are developed from ordering units and totalities (amounts). By formulating questions the different types of calculations arise. These must be practiced orally at first. Differentiating types of calculations according to temperaments is developed in group discussions. Acting out small skits on temperaments and tales of different temperaments in combination with physical exercises are very stimulating. Above all one must avoid identifying prematurely the different forms of questions with +, −, x, ÷ symbols. It should all still remain quite fluid.

A second approach is practiced at the same time (for instance during rhythmical exercises). It addresses the will and rhythmical system. This is based on a rhythmical differentiation over time (one, two, three . . .), arranged by numbers. Much can be accomplished with conceptually slower children by means of such exercises. It is always important to not only grasp time as rhythm, but to use every hour of instruction to calm the body down and to transition from the rhythmic activity to a conscious grasp of particular numbers. Counting is practiced in chorus as well as individually, at first up to twenty, then perhaps up to one hundred. There is no fixed deadline. In preparation for rhythmic counting, verses with particular rhythms may be brought into play.

A very popular and quite variable exercise is "guessing numbers." One employs different senses to determine numbers (hearing, sight, touch, and so forth). Guessing the number of fingers and toes is great fun. All in all, in order to calculate, the child must be sensitive to the periphery of his body.

In order to train memory the small "one plus one" and the first multiplication tables should be learned. Here not just the rhythmic but also the time memory should be nurtured. (See Steiner's *The History of the World Illuminated by Anthroposophy* [Die Geschichte der Welt in Anthroposophischer Beleuchtung] GA 233, first lecture).

Addressing analytic and synthetic thinking, formation of memory and working with the temperaments are of importance methodically. Quite early on differentiated abilities can be noticed, in a way similar to teaching music. These demand conscious inner differentiation of the way one teaches, yet they enable the children to support each other unconsciously in a wonderful way. One has to pay attention to a healthy balance between the children's incarnation and excarnation in mathematics. Here one may allow things to be livelier than usual. Drawing of forms may be an equalizing resource with individual manual activities as long as written calculations are still in the background. The teacher needs to have a competent overview of computing operations, and he must keep in mind the transition to the decimal system. The decimal system is a practical aid in dealing with numbers. It is, however, not part of the nature of numbers.

Preparation for geometry belongs to form drawing and eurythmy. Teachers interested in the subject may find a resource in the geometric laws of one-dimensional curves. The book by E-M. Kranich, M. Jünemann and also the book *Form Drawing* by E. Schuberth and L. Embry-Stine contain information on this subject.

Literature

To awaken a sense for the beauty of computing it pays to read the foreword and the introduction to *Arithmetic and Algebra* by Louis Locher-Ernst. The fourth and twelfth chapters may help as orientation.

The following are also recommended: Louis Locher-Ernst, "On the Relation of Mathematics to Art and Religion," in *Mathematics as Preschool of Spiritual Cognition* [Mathematik als Vorschule zur Geisterkenntniss], Dornach: 1973; Ernst Bindel, *Calculation, Anthropological Basis and Pedagogical Significance*, also an *Overview of Mathematics in Waldorf Schools During the First Five Years of School,* [Das Rechnen. Menschenkundliche Begründung und Pädagogische Bedeutung. Zugleich ein Überblick über das Rechnen auf den Waldorfschulen in den ersten fünf Schuljahren], Stuttgart: 1982; Ernst Schuberth, *Teaching Mathematics for First and Second Grade in Waldorf Schools* and with Laura Embry-Stine, *Form Drawing : Grades 1- 4.* Suggestions on teaching mathematics by Rudolf Steiner may be found in the collection by U. Kilthau and G. Schrader, already mentioned.

Second Grade

During the second year of school the children should become totally secure in the small multiplication tables. It is important to make sure that the multiplication tables are not simply recited rhythmically but that questions can be answered completely, for example: What is six times seven? What is forty-two? One can start working with a series of numbers (twos, threes, etc.) with such problems as: When do the threes and fours sound together? Rhythmical work with numbers also yields a feeling for their individuality. For example, "48" is a rich number, a "kingly number," because many numbers are contained in ("reigned" by) it. "47" is a "beggar's number" (a prime number). Many imaginative ways of presenting numbers are available. Calculations can still be practiced predominately within one hundred. In these exercises one should still connect calculations to concrete events using stories. Of course there are really no boundaries for counting. Now analytical and synthetic computing operations can be completely captured in writing.

In form drawing bilateral symmetry is practiced (mirror symmetry). The basic geometric forms of the triangle, quadrangle, circle, and ellipse will appear in the process.

Literature

As suggested for the first year of school.

Some technical fundamentals on a theory of numerical rhythms can be found in *Arithmetic und Algebra,* chapter 33, particularly p. 264, albeit the form of presentation is still far removed from the school. Louis

Locher-Ernst's short essay "The Series of Natural Numbers Seen as a Work of Spiritual Art" [Die Reihe der natürlichen Zahlen als Geistkunstwerk] is also helpful. Form drawing as suggested for the first grade.

Third Grade

Home building and husbandry introduce a strong everyday life and practical element to the curriculum. Dealing with measurement (feet, yards, pounds, meters, kilograms, etc.) leads to simple calculations of sizes. Measuring and subdividing become very distinct from each other when dealing with different magnitudes:

$$6m \div 3m = 2 \quad \text{and} \quad 6m \div 2 = 3m$$

Written calculations are, as a minimum, used for addition and subtraction. Here our decimal system with the place values plays an essential role.

The large multiplication tables are being learned. Special series of numbers, such as squares, can also now be memorized. Beautiful relations between numbers should become visible during the exercises. Much could now be borrowed from subjects to be taught later on, in much the way Louis Locher-Ernst does in the introduction to his book. For instance, if one looks at the problems: $10 \cdot 10, 9 \cdot 11, 8 \cdot 12, 7 \cdot 13$ and so on, the sum of factors always stays the same (20), yet the product gets smaller. What laws are hidden in the results? More gifted children gnaw with enthusiasm on such a problem.

The teaching of rhythms, the sounding together and "harmonizing" of rhythms, and the discovery of the individuality of numbers out of their multiplicative relations are deepened. For example, four- and sixfold rhythms sound together in the twelvefold rhythm. The four- and sixfold rhythms are being "harmonized" by the twofold rhythm; this one counts both within itself. Thus:

$$4 \cdot 6 = 2 \cdot 12$$

Complicated problems of symmetry can be posed in form drawing. Steiner suggests treating them by drawing "free symmetries." The teacher should be technically knowledgeable of the different forms of symmetries (mirror symmetry, multiple symmetry axes, rotating symmetry, possibly symmetry on the circle, inversion). But all of this must be created artistically and out of a direct form-experience.

Literature

The fourth chapter of *Arithmetic and Algebra* deals with the formation of a numerical system. The non-decimal ranking systems discussed there are not yet a part of the curriculum, but the teacher should have a background understanding them. On page 43 written multiplication is briefly mentioned. One finds another clear explanation of measurement and subdividing in Chapter 16. Chapter 29 contains material on equations of magnitudes. It is still early, however to treat magnitudes algebraically. A suggestion on the subject of numerical rhythms may be found in E. Schuberth's *A Story for Calculation* [Eine Rechengeschichte]. One can also nurture numerical relationships by playing the card game "Multiplex."

Synopsis

The first three years of schools form a unity in some respects. They are characterized by dealing with natural numbers in concrete or concretely imagined situations. One moves between a more imaginative and a more musical element as one ties down quantities and calculates with them on one hand, and on the other considers numerical relationships and rhythms. The calculations are conducted within a minimum of 1000, but the numerical area up to 100 or 120 should be easily comprehensible within the children's minds by the end of the third school year. Many things can still be supported by rhythmic motion exercises. Up to the first "Rubicon," constitutional weaknesses (calculating weaknesses) can still be worked on successfully with the class in unison.

Geometry is artistically nurtured within the framework of drawing forms. This leads to both a knowledge of basic geometric forms and training the sense for symmetry with all its educational effects.

Fourth Grade

The children having crossed the first "Rubicon," the most important new impact of the mathematics curriculum is calculating with fractions. In many respects one can start by repeating the first part of grade one, namely to create parts from the whole. In contrast to grade one we now observe the relationship of the parts to the original entity. This yields the concepts of stem fractions. One should avoid using only one image to illustrate geometric fractions (a cake or a circle). One can form quarters from triangles as well.

After dealing with stem fractions, fractions with the same denominator are added or subtracted. Enlarging or shortening make it possible to add originally "dissonant" fractions like $\frac{1}{2}$ und $\frac{1}{3}$. The rhythmic exercises with numbers of grade 3 can now be used as a basis for further developments. Twofold and threefold rhythms sound together in the sixfold one. The conversion of halves and thirds into sixths makes addition possible. Enlarging and shortening signify transition from larger to smaller units and vice versa. This may be interpreted rhythmically as well.

The difference between measuring and dividing continues to play an important role. Dividing magnitudes leads to addition and subtraction, measuring to multiplication and division of fractions.

Decimal fractions are introduced as practical conventions. They allow one to widen and continue calculations with liters, meters, etc. Written calculations in this area can be introduced and/or strengthened, insofar as this has not been done already.

In geometry description of shapes is now added (descriptive geometry). Quadrangles, triangles, the circle, the ellipse can be characterized very well based on creating them by drawing with observant judgment. Observing the sides, angles and symmetries is still unconnected with later procedures of proving; rather they serve the ability to describe direct experience.

Steiner considers the nurturing of spatial mental pictures to be very important. He uses the example of the elliptical shadow of a sphere on a level plane. Instructive conversation and demonstrations are well suited to awaken simple mental pictures of spatial relationships in the children without actually going into descriptive geometry.

Literature

Fractions are discussed in Chapters 25 and 26 of *Arithmetic and Algebra*. The schools still do not use algebraic notation. The rules have been developed, formulated and conveyed to memory in words.

The teacher should have a thorough technical understanding of the connection between ordinary fractions and decimal fractions, as well as having thoroughly studied how to introduce computing operations. The relationship between fractional and proportional numbers is carefully worked out in Chapter 26. Some important remarks on calculating with fractions are to be found in Steiner's lecture "Renewing the Art of Didactical Pedagogy through Spiritual Science," [Die Erneuerung der pädagogisch-didaktischen Kunst durch Geisteswissenschaft], lecture 14, GA 301.

Fifth Grade

The demands of grade four continue to be considered. The following skills should be attained: conversion of fractions to decimals and vice versa, shortening complicated fractions by taking numerator and denominator apart into prime factors, addition and subtraction of fractions in difficult cases by systematically determining the prime denominator, all degrees of difficult calculations of fractions with applications. Examples of applications may be largely taken from everyday life. In addition to all this the children should practice "free" mathematical activity through mental arithmetic and the observation of numerical relationships when taking prime factors apart.

Simple calculation of proportions should be practiced. Here the schooling of a sense of dependencies (e.g. quantity–price) should be stressed. "Estimate first, then calculate" creates assurance when dealing with numbers. The "Rule of Three" is a special case of proportional calculation. It is beneficial for sixth grade readiness if simple percentage calculation is taken up at this time.

In geometry the child is led to exact form. Forms and figures should appear immersed in fluid motion in this process. Simple basic construction with compass and ruler are carried out with enthusiasm at the end of the fifth grade. Geometry should culminate with the special case of the Pythagorean theorem for the equilateral triangle.

All in all, geometry may assume a very "workmanlike" character. One can, for instance, talk of the Pythagorean string used by the Egyptians to create the right angles on the foundations of their pyramids. One can cut out triangles and fold them.

Literature

One can add the first parts Chapters 29 and 30 of *Arithmetic and Algebra,* mentioned before for the fourth grade, assuming that the teacher sees the subject matter in a wider connection.

A number of stimulating publications for beginning geometry are available: Alexander Strakosch, *Introduction to Geometry by Practicing Observation,* [Einführung in die Geometrie durch übende Anschauung], Stuttgart: 1962, and Gerhard Ott, *Geometry for the Classroom Teacher of 6th, 7th, and 8th Grade* [Geometrie für den Klassenlehrer der 6, 7, und 8 Klasse], available from Helmut Wagner, Rudolf Steiner Schule, Endstrasse 100, A -1238 Vienna. For geometry one should reread Stockmeyer's accounts in *Rudolf Steiner's Curriculum.*

Sixth Grade

A new phase in the structure and methodology of instruction begins with sixth grade. From now on the child needs to be focused on the outer world in a very different manner. In conversation one can connect interest calculation with the monetary system, today's credit system and questions of the social threefold order. Medieval interest conventions merit their own study. (See for instance Herbert Hahn, *The Wellspring of The Soul,* [von den Quellkräften der Seele], Stuttgart: 1990.) Against this social background the interest formula ceases to be purely mathematical and becomes a social matter. The essence of an algebraic formula, of "letter calculation," is the articulation of a concept of connections conforming to some law. This lays the foundation for conceptual thinking rather than one tied to mental pictures. This is why instruction must not be abstract. The child should go through the process again and again: discussing a concrete problem (interest), solving the problem, verbalizing conformance to laws during the process of solving the problem, and finally experiencing the many applications of the laws thus uncovered.

But percent and proportional calculations must precede interest calculations which Steiner has emphasized. Now the opposed proportion is being included. Thence one proceeds to interest, discount, and promissory note calculations. These form the basis for "letter calculation."

It is a good idea to go to the bank and ask to be shown how promissory notes and discount are calculated. One can fill out forms with the children and discuss all together much that bears on business (e.g. postal orders, credit cards and more). I would invariably deal with algebraic formulas in a way to ensure that they describe verbally expressed conformities to laws.

At the end of the school year one can take up the transition to algebra of the seventh and eighth grades by presenting the rules for fractions in algebraic form. For instance:

$$\frac{a}{c} + \frac{b}{c} = \frac{a + b}{c}$$

As a conclusion, the decimal measuring system can be dealt with, appropriately for this level. Measures for length, area, cubes, weights, are to be written in decimal form. Conversions, rounding up and down, and measures of time are considered and worked with.

In geometry the first real proofs are presented. Steiner has repeatedly described proofs for the Pythagorean theorem (for instance during seminary discussions). A real understanding of the rules of congruity is now possible because position in space and form can be separately comprehended. However justified Euclidian geometry may be at this age, it would be desirable for teachers to acquire the basis for space and counter space. "Hull" and "kernel" may be discussed with children; they bring geometry into the living connections of projective geometry. An initial lesson on projection and shadow is added to this, where one talks about "shaped or sculpted space content," i.e. about light and shadow space (Rudolf Steiner, *Conferences* on January 16, 1921). It should all be as practical, concrete and well-illustrated as possible. For instance, one could practice spatial relationships by discussing the phases of the moon and the beginnings of finding one's way in the starry sky. Steiner emphasized in the course in Dornach of 1923 that any teaching of linear perspective should be preceded by a sense of color perspective.

Literature

In addition to the resources noted above one should continue to use the literature for fourth and fifth grades, from *Arithmetic and Algebra.* Locher-Ernst deals with the interest formula on page 17. It is also recommended to acquire a commercial book on practical interest calculation. Of course today much is being done by computer, but one can certainly still find literature about manual accounting. As far as geometry is concerned, we would particularly recommend the writings of Gerhard Ott. On a demanding level we have Locher-Ernst's *Space and Counter Space*, Dornach: 1988, AWSNA Publications. Georg Adams gives an understandable explanation in his short essay *Etheric Space* [Von dem Ätherischen Raum], Stuttgart: 1981.

Seventh Grade

Seventh grade deals with algebra proper. In class conversations one can work out the relations between addition and multiplication, subtractions and division in accordance with Steiner's suggestions. As one writes this down one also finds the appropriate transition to the higher types of calculation, namely raising to a higher power, root extraction, and eventually even logarithms (the latter only in their simplest form). In becoming conscious of computing laws (substitution, distribution, etc.) one learns algebraic conversion and calculating with common numbers, i.e. reducing, dissolving brackets, multiplying numbers with bracketed numbers and bracketed numbers with each other, and so on. Numbers would always be substituted for letters for proving. The binomial formulas $(a + b)^2$, $(a − b)^2$, $(a + b) \cdot (a − b)$ and eventually even $(a + b)^3$ can be practiced with many applications.

These formulas can be used to substantiate the root algorithm. Steiner considered the latter of such deep importance that it should, whatever come, be treated with great care, even if pocket calculators make it easy to look up roots. Algorithmic calculation increases in importance today. It may be practiced with lists of numbers having an inner law-based structure.

Negative numbers should be introduced in a manner that creates a feeling for the different quality of this domain of numbers. *In no case* should one start from geometrical pictures of what is negative (number line, thermometer). Debts that do not exist as actual coins but are valid just the same, give an appropriate picture for the negative quality. Debts are always being created among human beings who have social connections. Steiner identifies the etheric realm as the real area for what is negative.

Linear equations with one unknown are introduced through practical problems. Inserting specific numbers (fractions and negative numbers as well) needs to be practiced especially. Causal thinking is to be practiced in a living way, when solving equations. This leads to four clear rules. One may: increase, decrease, multiply, and divide both sides of an equation by the same amount. (In the last case zero is excepted.)

Equations should be expressed in words as well. One must be able to establish equations in accordance with a simple text.

In geometry first quadrangles and then triangles are calculated. The congruent formations of moving in one direction, turning, mirroring and centered symmetry help in many ways with proofs. Conversions of areas (to the degree they are needed to calculate areas) are carried out for the square, rectangle, parallelogram, trapezoid, rhombus and triangle. All many-sided, practical applications!

The remarkable points of a triangle should be discussed in constructive geometry, namely center of circumference, point of intersection of heights, center of gravity, center of internal circle, this with reference to Euler's straight line. Again one stimulates fluid imagination as one follows the path of these points during conversion of triangles.

The Pythagorean theorem and the propositions of Pythagoras must be taken up again. The Pythagorean theorem must be used along with root extraction to calculate lengths:

$$c = \sqrt{a^2 + b^2} \quad \text{or} \quad a = \sqrt{c^2 - b^2}$$

This liberation from two-dimensional thinking and the use of the Pythagorean theorem to measure lengths must be very carefully discussed. It creates difficulties to start with. Intersection of bodies like the cylinder and the cone are recommended for drawings. Perspective is being created.

Literature

Chapters 5–19 in *Arithmetic and Algebra.* The root extraction symbol is discussed in Chapter 30 on page 216. There is also a thorough presentation on this subject by Ernst Schuberth. On page 234 the abbreviated root algorithm is also discussed. Fundamentals for linear equations are found in Chapters 46–49. A particularly beautiful presentation regarding equations is found in Ernst Bindel, *Arithmetic, Anthropological Basis and Pedagogical Significance* [Die Arithmetik, Menschenkundliche Begründung und pädagogische Bedeutung], Stuttgart: 1967. The books by Arnold Bernhard are available for geometry and algebra of the seventh and eighth grades. Besides this we refer again to Gerhard Ott. A book on algebra by Ernst Schuberth is in progress.

Eighth Grade

The themes of the seventh grade are continued and widened to cover more difficult tasks. In seventh grade many areas were presented in the simplest form. It should all be repeated and practiced. In particular everything in connection with the teaching of equations should be continued (common solutions of linear equations with one unknown, equations with two unknowns). It is quite possible and desirable to work with non-equations. Mixed calculations are very salutary.

Calculating configurations and areas as well as determining volumes are continued or introduced within geometry. The most important curves can be discussed as "geometrical loci" in a constructive manner in connection with calculations that are being dealt with (parabola, ellipse, hyperbola, Cassini curves, division circle). Within the framework of geometry many teachers also deal with platonic solids.

Literature

Same as in the seventh grade, but add Chapter 50 of *Arithmetic and Algebra*. On the subject of curves refer to: Steiner, *The Path to a New Style of Buildings* [Wege zu einem neuen Baustil], GA 286, Dornach: 1982, and Louis Locher-Ernst, *Geometry in the Realm of Most Important Curves* [Geometrisieren im Bereich wichtigster Kurvenformen], Dornach: 1988. The platonic solids are newly presented in Paul Adams/Arnold Wyss, *Platonic and Archimedean Bodies, Their Starry Forms and Polar Formations* [Platonische und Archimedische Körper, ihre Sternformen und Polaren Gebilde], Stuttgart: 1994.

Endnotes:

1 Schuberth, Ernst. *Teaching Mathematics for First and Second Grades in Waldorf Schools,* Fair Oaks, CA: Rudolf Steiner College Press, 2000.

2 See for instance: Stefan Leber, *The Pedagogy of the Waldorf School and Its Basis,* [Die Pädagogik der Waldorfschule und ihre Grundlagen] Darmstadt: 1983. Also: *The Understanding of the Human Being in Waldorf Pedagogy* [Die Menschenkunde der Waldorfpädigogik], Stuttgart: 1993. Ernst Schuberth, *Education in a Computerized Society* [Erziehung in einer Computergesellschaft], Stuttgart: 1990, and more.

3 Arnold Bernhard. *The Basis for Algebra for Sixth and Seventh Grade at Waldorf Schools* [Algebra für die siebente und achte Klasse an Waldorfschulen}, Stuttgart: 1993; also: *Projective Geometry, Developed by Drawing from Beholding Space* [Projektive Geometrie. Aus der Raumanschauung zeichnend entwickelt], Stuttgart: 1984. Ernst Bindel, *Arithmetic, Its Anthropological and Pedagogical Significance* [Die Arithmetik, Menchenkundliche Begründung und pädigogische Bedeutung], Stuttgart: 1967; also: *Calculating: Anthropological and Pedagogical Significance* [Das Rechnen. Menschenkundliche Begründung und pädagogische Bedeutung. Zugleich ein Überblick über das Rechnen auf den Waldorfschulen in den ersten fünf Schuljahren], Stuttgart: 1982; also: *Logarithms for All: Elementary Introduction Indication of Higher Conformities to Laws,* [Logarithmen für jedermann. Elementare Einführung mit Hinweis auf höhere Gesetzmässigkeiten], Stuttgart: 1983. Louis Locher-Ernst, *Arithmetic and Algebra,* Dornach: 1984; also: *Geometric Exercises within Most Important Curves: A First Introduction to Geometric Thinking,* [Geomet- risieren im Bereich wichtigster Kurvenformen. Eine erste Einführung in das geometrische Denken], Dornach: 1988; also: *Projective Geometry and the Basis of Euclidian and Polar Euclidian Geometry* [Projektive Geometrie und die Grundlagen der Euklidischen und Polareuklidischen Geometrie], Dornach: 1988; also: *Space and Counter Space: Introduction to the New Geometry,* AWSNA Publications, 2002.

4 From a slightly different point of view one could perhaps compare the age in question with the tulip, youth with the rose. The leaves of the tulip, initially green, take part in the photosynthetic process of building and are gradually saturated with color. The petals of

the rose never take part in the the vegetative process of the green leaves. They develop protected by the shield of the sepals.

5 See to the development of logical thought: Martin Wagenstein's *The Pedagogical Dimension of Physics* [Die pedagogische Dimension der Physik], Braunschweig: 1976.

6 See for instance Mary Ann Pulaski, *Piaget*, Frankfurt: 1976, p. 323. This book gives a short introduction to Piaget's work.

7 Rudolf Steiner, *The Art of Education Methodological and Pedagogical Aspects* [Erziehungskunst Methodisch-Didaktisches], GA 294, Dornach: 1990, 8th lecture p. 112.

8 Ibid., p. 114.

9 Rudolf Steiner, *General Anthropology as a Basis of Pedagogy* [Allgemeine Menschenkunde als Grundlage der Pedagogik], GA 293, Dornach: 1992.

10 *Der Geometrieunterricht an Waldorfschulen, Band 3: Erste Schritte in die beweisende Geometrie für die 6. Klasse.* Verlag Freies Geistesleben, Stuttgart: 2001.

11 See note 9, first lecture.

12 See p. 5.

13 A more detailed description may be found at the end of this book.

14 See note 1.

15 In this connection see Ernst Schuberth, "Math Difficulties – Diagnosis, Symptoms and Therapy," in: *Developmental Insights – Discussions Between Doctors and Teachers,* David S. Mitchell, ed., published by: The Association of Waldorf Schools of North America, 3911 Bannister Road, Fair Oaks, CA, 2002.

16 Rudolf Steiner, *The Art of Education Methodological and Pedagogical Aspects* [Erziehungskunst Methodisch-Didaktisches], GA 294, 14th lecture, p. 191.

17 Rudolf Steiner, *The Art of Education, Seminary Discussions and Curriculum Lectures* [Erziehungskurs, Seminarbesprechungen und Lehrplanvorträge], GA 295, Dornach: 1984. Second curriculum lecture p. 168, also see the 13th seminary discussion.

18 An attempt has been made in the Appendix to sketch the significance and the interweaving of the basic social processes.

19 Rudolf Steiner: *World Economy* [Nationalökonomischer Kurs], GA 340, Dornach: 1979, 14th lecture.

20 Around 1074 Hayams' work *Risala fi-l barajin 'ala masajil al - Gabrwa -l maqabala* [On the proofs of algebra and almukabala].

Almukabala (juxtaposition, comparison) means collecting of parts of the same type, al - Gabr (filling up) the addition of members with the magnitude of the substracted size, this on both sides of the equation. The latter concept may have originated in Babylon. From *Biographies of Important Mathematicians* [Biographien bedeutender Mathematiker. Eine Sammlung von Biographien], hrsg. von Hans Wußing und Wolfgang Arnorl, Köln: 1978, p. 72.

21 The disease stemmed in part from the inappropriate pricing methods which failed to represent the cost of production, and also a quantity of available money which failed to correspond to the available goods and services.

22 If one wants to deal with the economics themes with some thoroughness, there will probably not be time for much percentage calculations. Therefore it is recommended to treat it in fifth grade or to pick it up in the framework of mathematical exercises. Since it is easily tied to fifth grade subjects, this is a good place for it and does not overburden the already great workload of sixth grade. Yet here we present the entire subject. (See p. 91.)

23 Such examples are of course unrealistic in many respects, yet they need to be used again and again in national economy. But they must not be overused and must contain the essential elements. If one would attempt to introduce all possible factors of human life, it would hardly be possible to obtain a clear picture.

24 Rudolf Steiner, *Economics* [Nationalökonomischer Kurs] (see also note 19), 6th lecture.

25 The following tabulation does not show all entries, since these are unimportant for what follows. Here we are interested only in the sum total. Of course, if friends wish to compare their entries by variations, they need the exact and complete entries.

26 Quoted from *Das Goetheanum*, No. 8, February 20, 1994. A detailed report was published in the *Süddeutsche Zeitung,* January 29, 1994.

27 Bernard Lievegoed, *Through the Eye of a Needle*, Stuttgart: 1992, p. 15.

28 We shall soon have to speak about the relation between work and income. The main object here is to present the transition from barter to money economy.

29 The cost of buying or leasing ground do not contradict this. These are created by human conditions of law and power and originate from human beings, not from nature. Furthermore, the fact that

damage to the natural environment can get to be expensive for humans in the long run does not belong in this context.

30 Adam Smith demonstrates with the example of a needle how great the savings are as a result of the division of labor. If a single individual were to carry out all the steps of producing such an item, needles would be impossibly expensive.

31 Luca Pacioli, *Treatise on Bookkeeping* [Abhandlung über Buchhaltung], 1494, Stuttgart: reprint 1992.

32 See Rudolf Steiner's *An Outline of Occult Science*, GA 13, Dornach: 1989, Chapter "The Nature of Mankind."

33 Ibid.

34 See Appendix.

35 See Rudolf Steiner's *Economics* [Nationalökonomischer Kurs], GA 340, Dornach: 1979, 12th lecture.

36 If necessary, the use of a bank account can be further explained to the children. Most children today know something about dealing with money through banks. The teacher can also use this opportunity to explain the origin of the word "bank." Like most expressions dealing with money it originates from the Italian for a large table (banca). When trading took place in Italian towns, or in other places in the past, many very different kinds of money came together. The money changers often traded currencies among themselves or loaned money. Thus, when one went "to the bank" one went to the table of the money changers.

The word bank has remained, even though nowadays the interior of a bank has a very different look and many more activities take place than was the case with the money changers. One has to differentiate between the "bank" and the park bench (German = Park bank). The English teacher (in a German school) can perhaps point to the fact that Americans have made a verb from the word "bank" which in Germany is used in the word "telebanking." This refers to the practice of dealing with money over the telephone or on the "web." The expression "Banker" came about through the flexibility Americans exercise with English.

37 Here we make *investment credit* our starting point. It expresses confidence in the recipient's future performance. We will address *consumption credit* later on.

38 From a management point of view one talks of the capital in use as assets (plant assets, assets in use = active side of the balance sheet).

Personal and foreign capital describe the middle origin (= passive side of the balance sheet). Here we are dealing with consumption and loan money.

39 See page 20 (in this document), paragraph 3.

40 This is the the way German banks calculate the number of interest days.

41 Goethe, *Faust II*, Act I, Emperor's Castle.

42 The media report 1.5 million households with excessive debts in 1994.

43 See Benedictus Hardorp's "Elemente einer Neubestimmung des Geldes und ihre Bedeutung für die Finanzwirtschaft der Unternehmung," a dissertation given at Freiburg in 1958, private printing by Hohensachsen in 1971.

44 More on this theme may be found in the Appendix.

45 See p. 62.

46 See the interesting discussions of Udo Herrmanstorfer, *Pseudo Economy: Labor, Land and Capital Cannot be Sold* [Die Unverkäuflichkeit von Arbeit, Boden und Kapital], Stuttgart: 1992.

47 See for instance B. Diepen/Herrling/Sauter, *Mathematics for the Banker* [Rechnen for den Bankkaufmann], Wiesbaden: 1987, p. 79.

48 When R receives the lumber he cuts out a sample to test the moisture content, weighs it and places it into a drying oven where all moisture is removed. Then he weighs the sample again. The difference is the weight of water. The moisture content is then determined by the formula:

$$\text{Moisture content} = \frac{(\text{moist weight} - \text{dry weight}) \cdot 100}{\text{weight after drying}}$$

49 If the note should have the value C_0 on the due date, then p is the discount rate and t the time to due date it has to be made out to the amount.

$$C_1 = \frac{C_0 \cdot 100 \cdot 360}{100 \cdot 360 - p \cdot t}$$

50 For example: Diepen/Herrling/Sauter, *Mathematics for the Bank Clerk* [Rechnen für den Bankkaufmann], footnote 47.

51 Michael Brater/Claudia Munz, *The Pedagogical Significance of Accounting, Discussions and Experiences with Their Application at the*

Waldorf School [Die pädagogische Bedeutung der Buchführung, Überlegungen und Erfahrungen zu ihrem Einsatz in der Waldorfschule], Stuttgart 1994.

52 Rudolf Steiner, *Spiritual Science and the Social Questions* [Geisteswissenschaft und soziale Frage], in "Luzifer Gnosis." Basic essays on Anthroposophy and Reports taken from the periodicals "Luzifer" and "Luzifer-Gnosis" [Geisteswissenschaft und soziale Frage, in: Lucifer-Gnosis. Grundlegende Aufsätze zur Anthroposophie und Berichte aus den Zeitschriften "Luzifer" und Luzifer-Gnosis"] 1903–1908, GA 34, Dornach: 1987.

53 Goethe *Faust II*, Act I, "Pleasure Garden," Penguin Classics, Baltimore: 1969, p. 75.

54 See Rudolf Steiner's *Economics,* footnote 19.

55 See p. 20.

56 See note 19.

57 Rudolf Steiner, *Toward Social Renewal,* GA 23, Dornach: 1976.

58 See Benediktus Hardorp, *Anthroposophy and the Threefold Order* [Anthroposophie und Dreigliederung. Das Soziale Leben als Entwicklungsfeld des Menschen], Stuttgart: 1986.

59 Adam Smith, *The Wealth of Nations. An Examination of Its Nature and Causes.*

60 J.P. Womack / D.T. Jones / D. Ross, *The Machine that Changed the World,* New York: 1990.

61 See for example: Stefan Leber, et al, *Economic Associations. Contributions to Brotherliness in the Life of the Economy* [Die Wirtschaftlichen Associationen. Beiträge zur Brüderlichkeit im Wirtschaftsleben], Stuttgart: 1987; Wolfgang Latrille, *Associative Economy, A Path to Social Renewal* [Associative Wirtschaft. Ein Weg zur sozialen Neugestaltung], Stuttgart: 1985; *Pseudo Market Economy*, Herrmannstorfer, Udo: Schein-Marktwirtschaft : Arbeit, Boden, Kapital und die Globalisierung der Wirtschaft / Stuttgart: Verlag Freies Geistesleben, 1997.

62 For example in Benediktus Hardrop, *Anthroposophy and the Social Challenge* [Anthroposophie und die sozialen Herausforderungen], Dornach: 1994.

63 Georg Unger, *The Formation of Concepts in Physics* [Vom Bilden physikalischer Begriffe], vol. 2, Stuttgart: 1961, p. 105.

64 Benediktus Hardorp, *Anthroposophy and the Social Challenges* [Anthroposophie und die sozialen Herausforderungen] footnote 62.

65 See footnotes 64 and 62.

66 Arranged by Ernst Schuberth with references to *Arithmetic and Algebra* [Arithmetik und Algebra] by Louis Locher-Ernst and similar writings.

Titles Available in English

The following titles are currently available in English, (ed.).

Anderson, Henning. *Active Arithmetic*, Fair Oaks, CA: AWSNA Publications, 1995.

Asten von, H. Keller. *Encounters with the Infinite, Grades 9–12*, (currently out of print but available in many teachers' libraries).

Baravalle, Herman von. *The Waldorf Approach to Arithmetic*, Spring Valley, NY: The Parker Courtney Press, 1996.

Edwards, Lawrence. *Projective Geometry*, Edinbugh, Scotland: Floris Books, 1996.

Franceschelli, Amos. *Algebra*, Fair Oaks, CA: AWSNA Publications, 1985.

_____. *Mathematics in the Classroom: Mine Shaft and Sunlight.* Spring Valley, NY: Mercury Press, 1998.

_____. *Mensuration*, Fair Oaks, CA: AWSNA Publications, 1987.

Harrer, Dorothy. *Math Lessons for the Elementary Grades*, Fair Oaks, CA: AWSNA Publications, 1982.

Jarman, Ronald. *Teaching Mathematics in Rudolf Steiner Schools*, England: Stroud, Gloucestershire, England: Hawthorn Press, 1998.

Kretz, Harry. *Solid Geometry: Geometry of the Platonic Solids and the Geometry of the Cylinder, Sphere, and Cone*, Fair Oaks, CA: AWSNA Publications, 1999.

Locher-Ernst, Louis. *Space and Counter Space*, Fair Oaks, CA: AWSNA Publications, 2002.

Mitchell, David, ed. *Proceedings from the Computer and Information Technology Colloquium*, Fair Oaks, CA: AWSNA Publications, 2002.

_____. *Proceedings from the Mathematics Colloquium*, Fair Oaks, CA: AWSNA Publications, 2001.

Rovida, Angelo Andes. *Projective Geometry*, Forest Row, England: Steiner Schools Fellowship, 1988.

Schuberth, Ernst. *Introduction to Advanced Arithmetical Operations for Waldorf School 7th Grades*, Fair Oaks, CA: AWSNA Publications, 2000.

_____, and Laura Embry-Stein. *Form Drawing: Grades 1–4*, Fair Oaks, CA: Rudolf Steiner College Press, 2001.

_____. *Teaching Mathematics for First and Second Grades in Waldorf Schools*, Fair Oaks, CA: Rudolf Steiner College Press, 2000.

_____. *The Geometry Lesson in the Waldorf School for Classes 4 and 5*, Fair Oaks, CA: AWSNA Publications, 2002.

Sheen, Renwick. *Geometry and the Imagination*, Fair Oaks, CA: AWSNA Publications, 2002.

Steiner, Rudolf. *World Economy*, London, England: The Rudolf Steiner Press, 1977.

Stockmeyer, E.A. Karl. *Rudolf Steiner's Curriculum for Waldorf Schools*, Forest Row, England: The Steiner Schools Fellowship, 1967.

Swanson, Herbert. *Geometry for the Waldorf High School*, Fair Oaks, CA: AWSNA Publications, 1987.

Ulin, Bengt. *Finding the Path: Themes and Methods for the Teaching of Mathematics in a Waldorf School*, Fair Oaks, CA: AWSNA Publications, 1991.